The

Legend Of

Luke Daisy

by Matthew Jay McCully

Chapters   Page

Chapter 1

A Miraculous Birth

"A baby is God's opinion that the world should go on." – Carl Sandburg

If you really stop to think about it, Luke Daisy should have never been born.

His mom and dad, Sarah and Scott, were both 40, and had been out of the baby-making business for ten years. Not only that, but Luke's dad had been vasectomized eight years before Luke was born. (I know some people would have thought the pregnancy suspicious, except that Luke looked exactly like his dad, and Sarah was, well, just not the type.)

I know a lot of this stuff – and I'm telling you it's all true, every word of it - because I was always Luke's best friend. My name is Michael Cateere, although Luke always called me Mouse. And my dad was Dr. Robert Cateere, who delivered Luke. (Of course this was before all of the babies were delivered by Amazon.) Dad is also the one who gave Mr. Daisy the vasectomy, although he never really liked to talk about that.

Nowadays I guess someone would be pretty likely to sue over a failed vasectomy, but not Mr. Daisy.

"That failed procedure is one of the things I am most thankful for," he would say. "One of my greatest blessings.

"It was clearly God's will," he would add. "And just another example of how God still does miracles."

Mr. Daisy talked often about God's will, what with being the pastor of our church and all. And I think he knew a thing or two about it. He read his Bible more than anybody I knew – seemed like he had the whole thing memorized. One thing I know he thought was God's will: love your family and friends and neighbors as much as you possibly can.

Once, I remember, he was taking Luke and me to the mall because we had saved up enough of our allowances to buy several packs of baseball cards. It was a Saturday and the mall was crowded, but when we pulled in there was a parking spot right in the very front. But Mr. Daisy just drove right past it.

"Hey Mr. Daisy, there's a spot right there," I said. But he just kept driving. "Why didn't you park there?"

Mr. Daisy waited until we had parked – a long way from the entrance, by the way – and then turned to us and said, "Think about how happy that's gonna make somebody else who finds that spot. Doesn't that make you feel kind of good? Besides, walking a little extra distance never hurt anybody, especially a couple of strong young boys and an old man who needs to lose a little weight."

That's what Mr. Daisy was like. He was this big man with a big beard and big, strong arms, and when I was little and would close my eyes and think about God, often the image of Mr. Daisy would pop into my head. I know that sounds kind of silly now, but when you're a kid … I don't know, it made me feel kind of safe to think of God that way.

My dad hardly ever talked about his work, even to my mom, but he loved to tell everybody the story of Luke's birth.

"People like to use the term 'miracle birth' a lot," he would say, "but in my 30 years of delivering babies this was the only one I was a part of.

"You gotta remember, it was 1956 and we didn't have all the technology and fancy instruments we have today. But we knew it might be a difficult delivery, what with Sarah being 40. But she was strong. Very determined. And she pushed Luke out.

"Well, almost all the way out. The last thing to come out was his hand, and wouldn't you know his hand was holding onto something. *His brother!* We had no idea Sarah was carrying twins, until Luke pulled his little brother out after him.

"We were all amazed, standing there looking like a bunch of goobers who had just seen a two-headed frog or something," he would laugh. "But then we could see that, although Luke was a strong, healthy baby, his little brother was not okay."

Dad would always shake his head then, and get a little teary-eyed before he'd continue.

"I guess when I saw him holding his little brother's hand I should have known that Luke would always be there to take care of him, and he sure was," dad would add with a smile. "So I tell people that I delivered Luke Daisy, but it was Luke himself who delivered his twin brother John Daisy."

And that's how the legend of Luke Daisy began.

Chapter 2

The Daisy Family

"Families are the compass that guides us. They are the inspiration to reach great heights, and our comfort when we falter." – Brad Henry

I was born a week after Luke and Johnny, so it's true when I say that I knew Luke my whole life. Our moms and dads were best of friends, so the three of us kids were almost always together. Luke was first to crawl, then me. Johnny never learned to crawl. Luke was first to walk and talk, then me. Johnny eventually learned to walk and sorta talk, although often Luke was the only one who could really understand him.

Nowadays we would say that Johnny was special needs. (I don't know. Seems like we all have special needs.) Before that people like Johnny were called disabled, or handicapped. But back in the early '60s, at least where we grew up in the Pacific Northwest, we just used the word retarded. Johnny was retarded. It didn't mean we didn't love him, because I think everyone who really knew Johnny loved him. He was the happiest, kindest boy I ever knew. No kid was ever loved more than Johnny Daisy. And nobody loved Johnny Daisy more than his brother Luke.

We grew up in a city called Bonney Flats, halfway between Seattle and Tacoma. It wasn't nearly as big as Seattle or Tacoma, but as Seattle stretched south and Tacoma expanded north, it became a pretty good-sized town in its own right. We had eight grade schools, four junior highs, and two high schools. There was a mall, twin movie theatres, several hamburger and pizza joints, a great hot dog stand (Bluto's), a large public pool, a huge lake in the middle of town, and most importantly, a lot of woods and trails and parks where fun-loving, adventure-seeking boys could play. It was a perfect place to grow up.

It seemed like most of the dads in Bonney Flats worked at Boeing, where they made airplanes, or Weyerhaeuser, where they made stuff out of wood. I always wondered if the two companies got together and made those little balsa wood airplanes that we would put together and see whose could fly the farthest, until they broke apart on the second or third flight. As a young boy it felt like we all had the same economic status, but now I realize that wasn't true. It was a pretty typical middle-class suburb: the dads went to work and did the yardwork; the moms took care of the houses, packed the lunches, fixed the dinners, helped with the homework, checked that we did our chores, and told us "wait 'til your father gets home" when a batted ball cracked a window.

Like I said, my dad was a doctor, so I guess we were upper-middle class, maybe even rich. Our house was probably the biggest in the neighborhood, and my folks drove pretty new cars most of the time. But I never really thought of us as rich. My allowance was the same as Luke's - $2 a week (if we did all our chores and weren't paying off a broken window) – so it just seemed like we were in the same boat.

Luke's dad was the pastor of our Baptist church, and looking back I'd have to say that the Daisy family would have been classified as lower-middle class. Their house was average size, but it seemed kind of small because it was always filled with people. And food. And music. Mrs. Daisy was a great cook – nothing fancy, just all the stuff that kids love: mac & cheese with cut-up hot dogs, tuna melts, nachos, chocolate chip cookies, etc.

And she could play the piano and sing better than anyone we knew. Luke and I didn't appreciate the music as much as we should - we were always too busy playing – but Johnny could sit for hours on the piano bench next to his mom listening to her play and sing. I wonder if it somehow made him remember being in the womb. Who knows?

Each of the Daisy family members was great in a different way. Mr. Daisy was a gifted speaker and Mrs. Daisy had her music.

Matthew, who was born on the same day Pearl Harbor was bombed (Dec. 7, 1941), got average grades, and he couldn't throw or catch a ball to save his life, but he could build anything and he could fix anything. And he loved to do those things for Luke and Johnny and me. He built us the coolest playhouse, and the greatest tree fort. He would fix our bikes or radios when they broke, and when we got old enough would keep our cars running smoothly. He wound up owning a chain of successful auto repair stores in the Puget Sound area and made a fortune, but still spent most of his days with greasy hands.

Mark Daisy, born five years later, was a genius. I mean, literally a genius. He was the first student ever from Paul Revere High School – go Minutemen – to get a perfect score on the SAT. He could do complex math equations in his head, and knew every formula for every possible math scenario. He wound up with a full ride scholarship to M.I.T., and eventually went to work for NASA, where at the age of 30 he was the lead scientist on the Viking 1 project, our first space probe to land and send back pictures from Mars. Mostly he left us alone and lived in his own little world of numbers, unless we needed help with our homework, which he would give, although to be honest, we often couldn't understand what he was trying to tell us. Oh, and in the late 90s he was a three-time winner on *Jeopardy*.

You know about Johnny. All smiles and tenderness. A lot of people felt sorry for Johnny, but Johnny never felt sorry for himself.

And then there was Luke. He was, simply, the greatest athlete anybody in and around Bonney Flats had ever seen. From the very start he was bigger, stronger, faster, tougher, and quicker than everyone else our age. He had the best hand-eye coordination, was the most agile, and had an uncanny ability to know where a ball was going to go before anybody else.

And he always won. I don't mean that most of the time he was on the winning team. I mean that, literally, HE ALWAYS WON! If it was a race, he finished first. If it was a team sport, his team came out on top. If it was any kind of a contest where athletic skill was involved, Luke won.

And we played it all: football, basketball, baseball, field hockey, bike races, running races, whiffle ball, tennis, ping pong, you name it. And when we weren't outside playing a sport, we were inside playing a game: checkers, Stratego, Life, Monopoly, Sorry, Pit, Battleship, Clue, Skunk, Lie Detector, Electric Football, Strat-o-Matic Baseball. Life was sort of a non-stop series of competitions for us. And the competition was basically to see who would finish second.

The only time Luke ever lost – besides a game of chance – was when he was up against Johnny. Luke never beat Johnny.

"Baba, Ah bitted Wookie in da wase," Johnny would rush into the house exclaiming. (Mama, I beat Lukie in the race.) "Nawdy ehse bitted Wookie." (Nobody else beat Lukie)

And nobody else did beat Luke.

Chapter 3

The Bus Ride

"Encourage the disheartened, help the weak, be patient with everyone." - I Thessalonians 5:14

Because he was so superior to everyone physically – and the toughest kid any of us ever knew - I'm sure a lot of people thought Luke was too tough to ever cry. But I saw him cry a few times.

I'll never forget the first time.

It was Labor Day, 1962, the day before our first day of school in first grade. Back in those days not every city offered kindergarten, so for us in Bonney Flats our first day of first grade was our first day of school ever. And the first time to ever ride a school bus.

Dad had been called out to the hospital because one of his patients had been in some kind of an accident, so mom and I were having dinner at the Daisy house. This was a fairly regular occurrence.

"So tomorrow morning, Michael and Luke, you'll catch the bus on the corner at 8:45," Mrs. Daisy explained to us. "Dad will walk you boys down there. Johnny, I'll walk you to your bus at 8:30."

"Wait. What?!" Luke asked, dropping his fork mid-bite. "Why can't Johnny ride with us?"

"Well, he has a different bus, and it leaves 15 minutes earlier. We talked about this, Luke. His school starts earlier than yours."

"Mom, why can't he just go to the same school …"

"Luke," his mom interrupted, raising her voice slightly, something she hardly ever did. "We've talked about this. Johnny needs to be in his own school."

A short, awkward silence followed.

Then, barely above a whisper, Johnny said, "Baba, Ah wahta go with Wookie." (Mama, I want to go with Lukie.)

"I'm sorry, Johnny," Mrs. Daisy said shaking her head. "You'll be fine on your own bus. It will take you right to your school. Luke's bus comes too late for your school, and it doesn't drop off at your school."

Johnny's special school was in a newer building, a couple of blocks away from our old grade school.

As Johnny walked away sadly, I saw the tears welling up in Luke's eyes. "Mama, he'll be scared on that bus without me," he said.

"Luke, I wish he could ride your bus, but it just won't work," she said. "He'll be okay."

She tried to sound convincing, but I don't think she was so sure.

It was quiet for a while, just Luke sniffling, when a thought occurred to me.

"Since Johnny can't ride our bus with us, maybe we could ride his bus with him," I said.

Nobody said anything, but they all looked at me. "Luke and I could easily get up 15 minutes earlier, and walking a couple of extra blocks to our school would be no big deal for us," I added.

"I guess that could work," Mrs. Daisy finally said, smiling. "If you boys really don't mind."

"Hey," I said. "We're brothers."

And so it was that Johnny, Luke, and I wound up riding the same bus – the special ed, or "short bus" – on our first day of school. Johnny was scared about being in school without Luke, so Luke thought it would help calm him if we sang "The Wheels on the Bus Go Round and Round." After three very long, tedious verses (the wheels had gone round and round, the wipers had gone swish swish swish, and the horn had gone honk honk honk), I was starting to regret my brilliant idea of riding this bus together.

But at the third bus stop, Johnny all of a sudden quit singing. A boy – maybe third or fourth grade – had gotten on the bus and he was crying. Seeing him, Johnny got up and walked up to his seat.

"Dohna ky," he said to the boy (Don't cry.) "Ahbee you fen." (I'll be your friend.)

And so he sat with the boy the rest of the way to school, and, mercifully, we didn't have to keep recounting the lyrical activity of the bus *("The kids on the bus said hip hip hurray.")*

The boy's name was Ryan Hosserous, and he became Johnny's bus companion for the next five or six years. Luke and I switched back to our regular bus the next day.

Chapter 4

First Day of School

"Stand up to your obstacles and do something about them. You will find that they don't have half the strength that you think they have." – Norman Vincent Peale

When we got off the bus that first day of first grade, there were a couple of third graders waiting there, sneering at us.

"Well, well, well, it looks like the retards have arrived," said the bigger of the two. His name was Bruce Junkers, and his buddy was Marv Snortberry. They lived a couple of neighborhoods away from us, but we had heard about them, and our parents had warned us to stay away from them. Bullies.

"What's your name, retard?" Junkers spat.

Johnny, who wasn't able to sense the malicious tone, stuck out his hand like he'd been told, and said, "Ah Johnny Daisy. Nisameeyou." (Nice to meet you.)

Junkers looked at Johnny's hand scornfully, like he was offering a dead stinky fish.

Luke turned to Johnny and said quietly, "Go on now, Johnny. You and Ryan go to school."

Johnny now sensed that there was trouble brewing and before he walked away said, "Dohna hurhim Wookie." (Don't hurt him, Lukie.)

Although Junkers was a pretty big third grader and two years older, he was barely taller than Luke, and not as broad in the shoulders.

"I said, what's your name, retard," Junkers said again, looking directly at Luke.

"My name's Luke Daisy."

Junkers laughed. "You ever hear a worse name than that, Marv?" Snortberry laughed along.

"You know," I piped up. "I wouldn't think two guys named Junk and Snort would be making fun of people's names."

"Shut up, punk!" Junkers shouted at me. "Besides, it's pronounced Young-ers, you idiot."

I think maybe I had touched a sore spot.

"Luke Daisy, huh?" he continued. "I think maybe I'll call you Puke Pansy. What do you think of that?"

"I think you'll only do it once," Luke said calmly.

I turned to look closer at Luke and I could see that all the light had gone out of his eyes, his body looked relaxed but his knees were bent a little and his right hand was beginning to curl into a fist.

Something about the way he said it made Junkers pause, and you could almost see his one or two functioning brain cells struggling to make a decision. He made the wrong one.

"Puke Pansy," he said, thrusting out his jaw and giving Luke a little shove.

They say that people who see a rattlesnake strike never forget it, the lightning speed is so remarkable. I don't doubt it for a second.

Luke's fist connected with Junkers' neck before anybody could even think about reacting, and that bully dropped to the ground like a sack of potatoes, grabbing his throat, writhing in pain, trying to yell "I can't breathe, I can't breathe," but all that came out was something like "Ahcabee, ahcabee."

Snortberry stood there for a second, mouth agape, and then turned to run. I didn't really plan it, but when he ran past me my brand new black Chuck Taylor Converse came slightly off the ground and poor Snortberry went sprawling hands and face first into the curb.

"I'm telling," he sniveled, in true beaten-bully fashion, as he ran off.

"What now?" I asked Luke, as we stood looking down at miserable Bruce Junkers.

"I guess we just go to our class," he said.

And so we turned and began walking the two blocks to Woodlake Elementary.

"Do you think every day will be this exciting?" I asked.

Chapter 5

Principal's Office

"Teach your children well." – Graham Nash

Our first day of school ended, as we feared it would, in the principal's office. Just before the final bell rang, one of the school secretaries came into our class and handed our teacher, Mrs. Tanner, a note. She looked up and said, "Luke and Michael, they want you two boys to go to Mr. Wood's office rather than catch the bus home. Your fathers are there, so they'll be able to drive you home."

I looked over at Luke, sitting at the next desk, and said quietly, "I think we're in big trouble."

He just kinda shrugged, as if to say, "Oh well, I guess we'll see."

When we got to the principal's office there were already seven people there, waiting for us, and they all looked up when we walked through the door. Both of our dads motioned for us to come sit in the empty chairs by them. Across from them sat Bruce Junkers and his dad, as well as Marv Snortberry and his dad. Mr. Wood sat behind his desk, hands folded on top of some papers.

"Well, I think everyone knows why we're here," Mr. Wood started, but he was quickly interrupted by Mr. Junkers.

"I want to know what you're going to do about these two punks hurting our boys," he shouted.

Jack Junkers was a small man – the smallest in the room. He wore a suit and tie, a lot of jewelry, and his jet black hair was slicked back. His face was red from being angry, which, I found out later, he often was. It turns out he was a big time real estate guy, probably the richest person in all of Bonney Flats. It seems he had inherited a lot of money from his rich grandfather, bought up a ton of land, and sold it for a huge profit to some big-time Seattle developers. He owned Junkers Realty, Junkers Savings & Loan, Junkers Clothing Store, and JJ's Auto Dealership (somebody wise convinced him that an auto dealership named Junkers probably wasn't a good idea). He was very used to calling the shots and getting his way, since many people in Bonney Flats were either employed by him or just plain intimidated by him and his wealth.

Unfortunately for him, he was in a room with three men who did not fit into that category.

"I want these boys suspended immediately," he continued with his rant.

Mr. Wood looked at him and sighed.

"First of all, Mr. Junkers," he said. "I am running this meeting. Not you. Do you understand that?"

"Well, I just want to make sure ..."

This time it was Mr. Wood who did the interrupting.

"Do you understand that?" he said louder and more forcefully.

Taken aback, Mr. Junkers squinted his eyes and nodded, almost imperceptibly.

Frank Wood was not someone you wanted to mess with. Then in his 40s, at 6-foot-4 and about 245, it wasn't hard to picture him as the 22-year-old Marine who had won the Medal of

Honor in World War II during his first combat operation. At the Battle of Mount Austen during the Guadalcanal campaign in the Solomon Islands in December of 1942, he repelled several Japanese banzai charges and rescued five of his fellow 7th Marine Regiment soldiers, all after being shot in the leg. He also earned the Purple Heart.

The biggest, strongest man any of us kids had ever seen, with hands the size of large plates, he almost always spoke in a soft voice, and usually with a smile on his face. He and his wife Kristen didn't have any children, but he loved the children of Woodlake Elementary. And he loved their house full of English Bulldogs – I think at one time there were 5 of them.

Years later when I had to do a high school history report on someone who had fought in World War II, I contacted Mr. Wood, who was still the principal at Woodlake. "I'm sorry, Michael," he said. "The war is something I just don't talk about. Too much killing. Too much sadness.

"But," he continued brightening. "If you ever need to do a report on bulldogs, I'm your man."

So now the room was quiet, and it was pretty clear that Mr. Wood was in charge. He paused for a few seconds, just to let that sink in.

"I've heard what Bruce and Marv have to say," he said. "Now I want to hear the story from you other boys. Luke?"

"Well," Luke began. "We had just gotten off the bus when Bruce started making fun of Johnny and I."

"Johnny and me," Mr. Daisy corrected.

"Yeah, Johnny and me. I asked him to stop. He wouldn't stop. So I hit him. Then he stopped. We were just minding our own business, trying to get to school."

"Did Bruce hit you first?" Mr. Wood asked.

"No," Luke answered. "He just kind of shoved me a little."

Mr. Wood then prompted me. "Michael?"

"Yeah, that's pretty much the way it happened," I said.

"And did you trip Marv?"

"Not on purpose," I said. "When he turned to run away because he was so scared, he just kind of tripped over my foot. No offense, Mr. Snortberry, but I don't think your son is very coordinated."

As I finished I caught a glimpse of Mr. Wood hiding his face behind one of the papers on his desk. It looked like he may have been trying to cover up a smile.

"This is ridiculous, Wood," Mr. Junkers shouted. "They're lying, and you'd better make sure they never touch our boys again."

That's when my dad piped in. "Are you saying, Mr. Junkers, that you want to be assured that our first grade boys will stop picking on your third grade boys?" he asked, feigning innocence.

This time Mr. Wood actually covered his mouth with his hand.

The whole time it was like a giant glaring contest. Bruce kept glaring at Luke, Marv kept glaring at me, and Mr. Junkers kept glaring at Luke's dad.

"All right," Mr. Wood said finally. "I've heard enough. Luke, you can't go around hitting people, even if you think they deserve it. You understand?"

"Yes, sir," Luke replied.

"And Mr. Daisy, I'll leave it to you to make sure Luke understands that, and you can decide on his punishment.

"Michael," he continued, turning to me. "I'm not really sure if you did anything wrong, but I just want to make sure you are taking this whole thing seriously."

"Yes, sir," I answered.

"Bruce and Marv," Mr. Wood went on. "Don't let me hear about you two trying to bully any more kids. If there's one thing I won't tolerate in this school it's bullying. You understand that?"

No answer.

"Do you understand?" he repeated, louder and more sternly.

This time both Bruce and Marv nodded reluctantly.

"And Mr. Junkers and Mr. Snortberry ..."

But again Mr. Junkers interrupted him, standing and yelling.

"Don't tell me how to raise my own child," he shouted. And then, pointing at each of us, "This is not over."

With that, the four of them got up and left the room.

"Well, I think that went well," Mr. Wood said. "Why don't you two boys go ahead and wait outside while I talk to your dads some more?"

As Luke and I headed out the door, we heard Mr. Wood start his conversation with our dads, calling them Bob and Scott. He knew them both well, since dad was his doctor and Mr. Daisy was his pastor. I don't think that hurt Luke and me at all.

On the drive home it was pretty quiet, although Mr. Daisy asked Luke to promise he wouldn't go hitting anybody again just because he was being teased.

"Dad, I won't hit anybody for teasing me," Luke agreed. "But I can't promise I won't hit 'em if they make fun of Johnny."

When we got back to our house, both our moms were there waiting for us.

"Michael, I'm having trouble believing that the Snortberry boy *accidentally* tripped over your shoe," my dad said. "Now you boys go outside while we decide what your punishment is going to be."

Luke and I headed out to shoot baskets, trying to figure out what our fate might be. Luke was afraid they would take away his balls – football, basketball, baseball – or not let him watch the college and NFL games on television on the weekends. I was afraid they were going to keep me from playing with Luke for a while.

Our biggest fear, though, was that they were gonna make us miss the World's Fair.

But a funny thing happened. Both sets of parents *forgot* to punish us after all.

Chapter 6

World's Fair

"While imagining a better future, let's also imagine a better self." – Vlad Zachary

In 1962 the World's Fair arrived in Seattle, and from April through October almost 10 million people went. For us kids, it was just about all we talked about. The first week there were live telecasts on *The Ed Sullivan Show*. Roy Rogers and Dale Evans, who we had watched on TV, put on their famous Western Show. The great Billy Graham was there. Officially titled *The Century 21 Exposition*, it promised glimpses into a science fiction future that had all of us kids crazy with excitement.

There was The Bubbleator, a glass elevator that rose one floor at the lightning speed of, well, an elevator. I still remember the recorded voice: "Please step to the rear of the sphere for a low-speed thrill ride to the world of tomorrow." It was an elevator that you could see out of, and your parents would let you ride by yourself, because they could see you. We thought it was the coolest thing. I think we rode it 24 times.

There was the Monorail. It was a train on elevated tracks that made you feel like you were flying through space. You could look down on the cars in the street. Awesome!

There was the Food Circus, with 52 places to eat. Mark Daisy pointed out that we could eat here once a week for a year and never repeat a meal. I dared Luke to eat the frog's legs, and he did it. He said he hoped it would help him jump higher, which, who knows, it may have (he was dunking a basketball at a pretty young age). It also made him a hero at Woodlake Elementary. *("Luke ate a frog!")* I settled for the famous Belgian Waffles, which made me feel quite the mature and sophisticated first grader, if you overlooked the syrup stain on my shirt.

There was the magnificent, futuristic Science Pavilion, which we had to drag Mark out of, and the Fun Forest, with its many rides and games, which they had to drag Luke and Johnny and me away from.

But of course the biggest attraction was The Space Needle. Built especially for the World's Fair in a little over a year, it was 605 feet tall and at that time the tallest building west of the Mississippi. It was, and still is, a thing of beauty that defines the Seattle skyline.

On the third Saturday of September the eight of us – mom and dad, Mr. & Mrs. Daisy, Mark, Luke, Johnny, and me (Matthew had gone earlier with some of his buddies) – piled into the Daisys' station wagon and made our way to Seattle for the great adventure. And most of the way us kids talked about the Space Needle, and what it would feel like to be at the top of the world. Maybe we could even eat at the restaurant there that actually revolved. A restaurant that moved! We could hardly wait. Luke wondered if they would let him climb the 848 steps instead of riding one of the elevators, and wondered how long it would take.

(They didn't let him climb that day, obviously, but in 1974 when he was a senior in high school and had achieved a great deal of fame for his athletic success, the Space Needle manager agreed to let Luke make the climb, and then it became an annual event. Luke made it in just over six minutes, which stood as the record for over 20 years until 1995 when a firefighter from Boise named Dave Thatcher broke it by three seconds.)

Getting to the top of the Space Needle was definitely going to be the highlight of the day. But when we got there, Johnny took one look and began to tremble and cry and refuse to go.

"Eeefahdow, eefahdow," he kept saying. (It fall down.) Johnny was pretty fearless most of the time, often to his own peril, but he was scared to death and there would be no talking him out of not going up the needle.

And his fear kind of made Luke a little hesitant.

"What if he's right, dad?" Luke asked. "What if it's some kind of, whaddayacallit, demolition?"

"Premonition," Mr. Daisy corrected.

"Yeah. Maybe it isn't safe," Luke added. "I'll stay down here with Johnny."

"Well we can't leave the two of you down here alone," Mrs. Daisy said.

"I'll stay with them," Mark offered. "I can go up next week with my friends. Plus, I want to do some calculations on what sort of wind resistance and vibrational offsets this thing has."

And so it was that, after all of our excitement, only the four adults rode to the top of The Space Needle that day. (I chose to stay with Luke and Johnny and Mark. After all, they were my brothers.)

Over the years, Luke and I had plenty of Space Needle rides, including one very bizarre triple-date in high school. Johnny never did go up, and the needle never did "fahdow."

Yet.

Chapter 7

<u>Dogs and Dynamic Duo</u>

"A boy can learn a lot from a dog: obedience, loyalty, and the importance of turning around 3 times before lying down." – Robert Benchley

In the fall of 1963 we started second grade, and again Luke and I were in the same class, sitting side by side. Johnny was doing well in his school, and even enjoyed riding the bus. He and his friend Ryan always sat together in the last seat where they could look out the back window and count how many animals they would see on the way to school.

"Wetaw teben day, WookieMow," Johnny might exclaim to us after school. (We saw seven today, Lukie and Mouse.) Johnny loved all the animals, and the neighborhoods in Bonney Flats had a lot of them. The pine trees were filled with squirrels, and some of them would eat peanuts right out of Johnny's hand. Nobody else's. Same with the ducks at Lincoln Lake, the biggest swimming area in Bonney Flats. Johnny would always bring some extra bread when we went there, and the ducks would start waddling towards him and surround him the minute we got off our bikes. Oh how those ducks loved Johnny.

Mostly Johnny loved dogs. And dogs loved him. Even the Schmidt's very large, very territorial German Shepard with the misleading name of Strudel. This Strudel was not sweet, but he looked at the rest of us as though we were sweet. As in, to eat. We all gave a wide berth to the snarling beast, who guarded the Schmidt's front yard on a chain that extended right to the edge of the sidewalk. But for some reason that dog loved Johnny, who would walk right over and talk gently to him while scratching his ears and belly. It was quite a sight. Johnny and the Schmidt's teenage son Jason were the only ones who Strudel didn't try to take a bite out of at one time or another.

Our dog was some kind of a mixed breed — maybe Cocker Spaniel and Labrador and Poodle *(a Cock-a-doodle?)* — that dad brought home from the pound and named Bonehead because he couldn't figure out the sliding glass door and kept knocking into it.

Bonehead wasn't very smart, but he was fast, and over the years Luke worked on his speed and quickness by chasing that goofy dog all over our back yard until they were both exhausted. In his sophomore year of high school basketball when Luke was named the league's Defensive Player of the Year, the local sports reporter looked very confused when Luke gave most of the credit to "my good friend Bonehead."

The Daisy's dog was a blind, three-legged Golden Retriever named Daisy Dog (Johnny named her, of course) given to them by a member of Mr. Daisy's congregation, Harry Orr.

Mr. Orr had been a popular teacher and coach at the high school, but when his wife and infant son were killed in a car accident, he began to drink heavily, and lost his job. Mr. Daisy was the one who stood by him through his whole ordeal and helped him "dry out" (the term they used back in those days). He actually came to live with the Daisy family for a year (this was several years before Luke and Johnny and I were born), and it was Mr. Daisy who went to the school board and encouraged them to give Mr. Orr another chance.

And the Bonney Flats school board never regretted that decision. Mr. Orr went on to be one of the winningest high school baseball coaches in Washington history, including a couple of state championships (more on that later), and in a story that came full circle, was Luke's high school baseball coach.

But back to Daisy Dog. Mr. Orr eventually remarried and started a new family, and their Golden Retriever Misty had a litter of eight puppies. The last born was a runt, born blind and without a left front leg. When the vet said it would probably be best to let that pup die, Mr. Orr objected.

"Coach Orr saw that this little pup was damaged and would need some extra special care," dad related to me years later. "And he said the best people he knew to help heal someone damaged would be the Daisy family. I don't think anyone would disagree with that."

And so from the time we were four years old, until his three legs finally gave out 12 years later, that sweet blind dog with a tail that seldom stopped wagging was one of our most constant companions.

Our second grade teacher was the wonderful Miss Cleveland. At just over five-feet tall and maybe 100 pounds she wasn't all that much bigger than her students, but she bounced around with such a high level of energy, and carried such an unmistakable aura of authority, that nobody was ever left in doubt about who was totally in charge. We had all heard stories about the famous "Cleveland Club," the stick she used to paddle seriously misbehaving students. It always leaned up against the chalkboard, and was the first thing you saw when you entered her classroom.

Remember, it was a different era, and hearing about some rotten kid getting a swat or two by a teacher or principal was not that uncommon, and usually with the parents' approval. One story that got passed down was that she swatted potty-mouth Pete Pearson so hard in January that he had to stand at his desk until March.

Years later she left teaching and became the first woman mayor ever in Bonney Flats, and after that the second female governor ever in the state of Washington, which surprised nobody. Our paths crossed when I was just out of college and I asked her about the stories of her legendary Cleveland Club. Were they true, or did she make them up herself to instill some fear and obedience into her young charges? She just gave me an enigmatic smile and with a twinkle in her blue eyes said, "What do you think, Michael?"

She was the best teacher we ever had.

Well, at the end of first grade they had decided to move Luke and me away from each other because apparently we talked too much. Miss Cleveland had us sit alphabetically, and much to our good pleasure, Cateere and Daisy wound up right next to each other.

It didn't take long for Miss Cleveland to realize that this might be detrimental to her educational purposes and something would need to be done. But rather than separate us, she came up with a plan of her own.

Before recess at the end of the first week of school, she called Luke and me up to her desk.

"Listen boys," she said. "It's clear to me that you two are the leaders of this class. All of the other kids look up to you and will pretty much fall in line with how you two behave. So I'm going to need your help.

"From now on, you Luke and Michael, will be my Dynamic Duo," she went on. "You'll set an example for the rest of the class on how to behave. You'll encourage the children that are afraid to participate, look for the kids at recess that are being left out and include them, and help me make sure the class is quiet when we're inside and it's time to learn. What do you think? Can I count on you two?"

There was no hesitation. "Yes, Miss Cleveland," we said in near unison.

Ever since he first showed up in comic books in 1940, I think every second grade boy had, at one time or another, safety-pinned a pillow case around his neck as a cape and pretended to be Batman, the mighty Caped Crusader, fighting off the Riddler or the Joker or the Penguin to save Gotham City. So the chance to be referred to as the great crime-fighting pair was an honor we weren't about to pass up.

"Wow! The Dynamic Duo," I said to Luke as we walked out to recess.

"I know. Pretty cool," he said.

"I guess I should start calling you Robin," I said, trying not to smile.

Luke just looked at me crossways with a crooked smile.

"Nice try, Boy Wonder," he said.

Chapter 8

The World Changes

"As human beings we have the most extraordinary capacity for evil." – Desmond Tutu

On a Friday afternoon in late November of that year we were sitting in class, doing multiplication flash cards, when the door opened and Principal Wood walked in. But instead of smiling at us and calling out "Hello my little spelunkers," like he usually did, he walked slowly over to Miss Cleveland and whispered something in her ear. Her eyes got wide, her mouth dropped open as her hands flew to her face, and she ran out of the room crying.

All 24 of us kids sat there in shock. Many, I'm sure, had never seen an adult cry, and probably none of us had ever seen a teacher cry.

"Boys and girls," Mr. Wood said quietly, in a moment none of us would ever forget. "I'm sorry to tell you that our president has been assassinated. You children will need to sit here quietly by yourselves for a few minutes until the busses come to pick you up and take you home."

And then he walked slowly out of the room. He had his hand up rubbing his forehead, but I could still see a tear running down the big man's face.

We sat there in stunned silence until Lindsey Patterson asked, "What does assassinated mean, Michael?"

When I explained, several of the girls started to cry. And sure enough, some of the knucklehead boys started to make fun of them and act up, taking advantage of the fact that we were unsupervised.

Luke would have none of it.

"Hey!!" he stood up and shouted, pointing his finger at the knucklehead ringleader. "Knock it off!"

I think it was the first time any of us had heard Luke raise his voice in anger. Silence ensued.

When the bus dropped us off, both my mom and Mrs. Daisy were at the bus stop waiting for us. Both had clearly been crying, but now did the stiff upper lip thing as they engulfed us in mama bear hugs. Johnny was there with them and he asked a question to which nobody knew the answer: "Whadey herhim, baba?" (Why'd they hurt him, mama?) He asked the same question again, twice, less than five years later. Again, there was no good answer.

Dad was still with patients, but Mr. Daisy was home in his study, and Luke and I were eager to talk to him to see if he could make any sense of it for us. He was on his knees praying when we got there, but he waved us in when he realized we were there waiting for him. He looked very old, and very tired.

"What's gonna happen, dad?" Luke asked.

"Well boys, Mr. Johnson will become the new president, they'll find out who did this terrible thing and punish him, and the country will move ahead," Mr. Daisy said.

"But it's kind of scary," I said. "And everybody's so sad. It doesn't feel like things will ever be normal again."

Mr. Daisy looked at me and nodded slowly.

"You're right, Michael," he said. "It's very sad and very scary. And it's a reminder to us that there is evil in this world. There is darkness. That's why we're called to be light."

"But," Luke hesitated. "what should we do?"

Mr. Daisy smiled sadly at his amazing son.

"Boys, the answer to that question is in that song you sing in Sunday School. *'This little light of mine. I'm gonna let it shine. Let it shine. Let it shine.'* God gave each of us special gifts. A light to shine. And that means being kind, being helpful, protecting the weak. Showing God's love to everyone. Maybe now more than ever."

He smiled and shook his head sadly.

"I don't think we're meant to understand why these things happen," he continued. "God doesn't promise us that everything will make sense. But He does promise us that He loves us and will always be with us. There's a verse in Isaiah 41 that says, 'Do not fear, for I am with you. Do not be dismayed, for I am your God. I will strengthen you and help you.' I think that's a very good verse for us to think about. Every day, but maybe especially today."

That was the first of many days where I could say "I'll never forget." Where I was, who I was with, what I was feeling. And almost all of those days I was with Luke.

Things did get back to normal quickly for us kids. Heck, two days later we were watching football on TV after Sunday School. For some reason the NFL decided to play their regular schedule, even though the nation was in mourning. We watched Roman

Gabriel lead the Rams to a 17-16 upset of Johnny Unitas and the Colts. We didn't have our own NFL team in Seattle, so a lot of us cheered for the Rams, since they were the team we got to watch most often on television.

The scary world had come crashing in on our carefree existence two days earlier, but now we were back to being kids again.

Chapter 9

Matthew Daisy

"Do not be overcome by evil, but overcome evil with good." –
Romans 12:21

"What should we do?" was Luke's question to his dad after President Kennedy was assassinated.

Matthew Daisy's answer was this: join the Peace Corps.

In President Kennedy's inaugural address in January of 1961 he issued his famous challenge*: "Ask not what your country can do for you. Ask what you can do for your country."* And then in March of that first year of his presidency he established the Peace Corps, designed to help third world countries with their social and economic development.

Matthew turned 22 a couple of weeks after the president was killed, and on his birthday, with his parents' blessing, he signed up for the Peace Corps, because he said he wanted to honor the slain president by making a difference in the world. After three months of training he spent two years in Tanganyika (now Tanzania) digging wells, building homes, and fixing every piece of heavy machinery that needed fixing.

When his two years were up he returned home to Bonney Flats for a few months, and then went into a Seattle Recruitment Center and, this time with his parents' very cautious blessing, joined the army. In 1966 that meant one thing: Vietnam. After his basic training at Fort Sill in Lawton, Oklahoma, Matthew had two tours of duty in the jungles of Southeast Asia, where he spent his time mostly carrying tools instead of weapons.

His job was to keep all the equipment running smoothly, a job he was naturally born to do. And so he worked on the M-48 tank; the M-113 armored personnel carrier; and the M-606 militarized jeep built by Kaiser. Towards the end of his time he also worked on the Bell UH-1 Iroquois "Huey" helicopters that were configured for troop transport and medevac roles. He liked to say that he thought his main job in the war was "saving American lives, not taking others."

But, like most every soldier of that time, he did see some combat. In the early months of 1968 he "saw the elephant" (first-hand combat experience) in the Battle of Khe Sanh, a bloody 77-day engagement where almost 600 Americans were either killed or wounded. Matthew was one of the wounded when some heavy artillery exploded near him and he lost all the hearing (permanently) in his left ear. He said he thought it was a fitting and ironic injury since "every teacher and girlfriend I ever had said I only heard about half of what they said."

The explosion and resulting hearing loss could have been Matthew's ticket home, but he didn't report it because he wanted to finish out his tour with his buddies. He spent his final six months overseas as a Forward Artillery Observer (FAO) on the Boeing B-52 Stratofortress.

The FAO's job was to use high-powered binoculars and night vision optics to report back to the bombardier whether or not his ordinance drop was on target. Much of the time the drop was successful, and the FAO would relay back, "Right on target!"

Matthew shortened his reports to an exuberant "Right on!" And then he started using the expression in his everyday conversation. When he'd call home and get an update on Luke's latest exploits, he would always say, "Right on!" Pretty soon his fellow soldiers started saying it, and of course we started saying it back home as well.

(And that, my friends, is the true story of how "right on" became a part of our common language. Thank you, Matthew Daisy.)

The war changed a lot of soldiers – understandably so – but Matthew returned with the same sense of tenderness and kindness and good humor that he left with. He didn't talk much about his Vietnam experience, but when he'd see us laughing at *Gomer Pyle* or *Hogan's Heroes* on television he might comment.

"It's okay to laugh at this stuff guys," he would say. "But don't forget: it's not real. War is definitely not a situation comedy."

Matthew Daisy was one of our heroes.

Chapter 10

Golf

"Golf is a puzzle without an answer." – Gary Player

"Golf is a game where you holler 'fore', hit six, and mark down five." – Paul Harvey

In 1964 the average eight-year-old was about 4 feet tall and weighed around 50 pounds. I was about as close to average as you can get. Luke, on the other hand, was the size of an 11-year-old. He was 4-foot-8 inches tall and weighed about 80 pounds. (I know these numbers because dad kept an accurate chart for all of us.) So he was taller and stronger than everyone our age, but to an even greater degree he was faster than all the other kids in the neighborhood.

In pick-up games on the playground, which included much older kids, even up to sixth grade, Luke was always chosen first. Didn't matter if it was football, basketball, baseball – you name it – he was the golden pick. Sometimes, even when there were several older boys, Luke was one of the captains. And his first picks would always be Johnny and me, even though everyone knew I didn't deserve to be a first- or second-round selection. I certainly didn't mind being on Luke's team, even if it was charity. It just meant I got to be at the front of the hose line with the other winning team members for our post-victory celebratory drink. We'd suck that cold hose water on a hot summer day and felt like we were drinking champagne out of the Stanley Cup. Sometimes, just to make the losers wait a little extra long to get their turn, we'd drink so much that our bellies would ache. But it was worth it.

In the summer of 1964 the Konsmo Corporation bought 100 acres of wooded land and turned it into the Bonney Flats Golf Complex. There was a pro shop, driving range, miniature golf, and a par-3 course, which was really not much more than a pitch-and-putt. All of the nine holes were between 60 and 90 yards, a great place for experienced golfers to work on their short games, and for youngsters and other beginners to get started learning to play.

My dad was a pretty good player — a single-digit handicapper — and he would play at the local public course most every Monday during the summer. His regular foursome included Mr. Daisy, a pilot friend named Mr. Coate, and another friend, Mr. Wolfe, who was an air traffic controller at Sea-Tac airport.

When the new golf complex opened, dad and Mr. Daisy thought it would be a good idea to take Luke and me out and teach us how to play. We got several buckets of balls and headed to the driving range first where they gave us some pointers: hold the club like this, position your feet like this, bend your knees just a little, gotta keep your head still, keep your left arm straight, eyes down but chin up, weight on the inside of your feet, bring the club back slowly, blah blah blah. All I could think was, "Please stop talking so I can start smashing these little yellow balls. How hard can it be?!"

As it turned out: very hard. At least for me. None of dad's advice sank in, leaving me to flail away in a very frustrating, unproductive manner.

Luke, on the other hand, listened intently to the coaching, and then when I started hitting my bucket of balls (trying to hit my bucket of balls), he just stood back and watched my dad hit. It was like he was trying to memorize the correct motions. Then he walked down the line watching other players hit balls, paying close attention to the guys who were hitting it well.

Finally (!!!) it was time to head over to the par-3 course. Mr. Daisy flipped a tee to see who would hit first, and it pointed to Luke. The first hole was 75 yards, and his dad handed him a 7-iron. Luke took two practice swings, which looked surprisingly like my dad's swing, stepped up to the ball and took a slow, smooth swing as if he was born with a golf club in his hand.

The ball went airborne, started a bit to the right but slowly curved back, bounced once, twice, and then rolled right into the cup. A hole-in-one!!!!! On his first swing ever.

(Remember I told you at the start, every word of this is true, even if it may seem hard to believe. Why would I lie? If I was going to lie I would say that it was me who got the hole-in-one. If you don't believe me you could ask my dad or Mr. Daisy. I don't think either of them ever told a lie in their whole life.)

"Holy cow!" dad shouted.

"That was amazing," echoed Mr. Daisy.

"Wow!" was all I could add.

"Did you see that?" shouted another man on the practice green.

We all just stared dumbfounded at Luke who seemed pretty calm.

"What?" he said with a sly smile. "Isn't that what you're supposed to do?"

Luke had three more hole-in-ones that day ..... no, I'm just kidding. That was the only one. But for the 9 holes he did have the lowest score of the four of us. Dad gave him a big pat on the back and congratulated him, although I think maybe he felt a little bad about losing to an 8-year-old first-timer. Mr. Daisy just shook his head and smiled — nothing Luke did ever surprised him. I don't remember Luke's score. I wish I did. The only reason I remember my score that day (97) is that Mark Daisy pointed out to me that it was the highest prime number under 100.

I figured this might be Luke's new favorite sport and I asked him if he was going to keep at it.

"Nah," he said. "There's no running. No jumping. No defense. No plays. No teamwork. I just don't think it's for me."

As far as I know, except for miniature golf, Luke never swung another golf club.

Chapter 11

Ken Carew

"As soap is to the body, so laughter is to the soul." – Jewish Proverb

In July of 1964, two months before we started third grade, the Carew family moved into the neighborhood, three houses down from us. They moved from Louisville because Mr. Carew was hired as a literature professor at the University of Washington in Seattle. He and Mr. Daisy had served in World War II together and kept in contact, with Mr. Daisy always encouraging him to move to the Pacific Northwest. They were the first black family in the neighborhood.

The Carews had 11 kids. Eleven!!! Ten girls and a boy. Ten girls!!! They weren't Mormon or Catholic, they just liked having kids, and having them all one year apart. They named them all alphabetically, Mr. Carew deadpanned, "so that I would be less likely to forget any of their names."

And so into our lives came Alice, Barbara, Carole, Debbie, Esther, Faith, Grace, Hope, Irene, Joy, and, finally a boy, Ken Carew. (Luke called him "Hoppy.")

Kenny was also eight years old, born exactly a week before Luke, two weeks before me. He was about half the size of Luke so he looked much younger, but he often reminded us that "you should really listen to me because I'm older and wiser than you two." To this day he is still the funniest person I have ever met, and he almost instantly became a best friend of ours.

The Dynamic Duo had just become the Three Musketeers.

Mr. Daisy always told us that we were all made for a purpose, and that purpose was to glorify God in all that we said and did. And he added that God gave each of us special gifts that we were to use to make the world a better place, and by doing so we would glorify God.

For a lot of people it wasn't hard to see the special gifts that God had given them. My dad could help heal people physically. Mr. Daisy could help heal people emotionally and spiritually. Mr. Carew could teach people. Mrs. Daisy brightened people's lives with her music. Luke's athletic gifts, we knew, would someday make him famous and the hero to thousands. I spent a lot of time as a kid wondering what my special gift was.

Ken Carew's gift was just as obvious as Luke's: he was put here to make people smile. He could sing and dance, and he could imitate just about anyone with his voice and mannerisms. He kept us in stitches.

If Mr. Daisy was preaching from Ecclesiastes 3 and quoted "To everything there is a season," Kenny would lean over and whisper, "Turn turn turn."

Some days he would decide to speak only in song titles and lyrics.

Me: "What a beautiful day."

Kenny: "Yeah. The sun is shining like a red rubber ball."

Luke: "What are you doing?"

Kenny: "Just groovin'. On a Sunday afternoon."

Me: "Can you come over and play?"

Kenny: "No, I'm grounded. I fought the law, and the law won."

Luke: "What did you do wrong?"

Kenny: "God only knows."

Me: "How long are you grounded?"

Kenny: "Until the year, 2525. If man is still alive."

Luke: "Did you cry?"

Kenny: "A little. 96 tears."

Me: "Well, we've got some candy for you when you're ready."

Kenny: "Great. You didn't have to be so nice."

Some days, especially as we got older, he would pour through the dictionary and thesaurus and decide to use as many big words as he could.

Me: "Man, that show was sure boring.

Kenny: "Yes. Prosaic. Quotidian. Mundane. Jejune.

Luke: "What?"

Kenny: "Pedestrian. Obtuse. Torpid. Ennuyant. Pedantic."

He also loved to throw out quotes from famous people into conversations, often Shakespeare, although I think he made up at least half of them.

Me: "I can't believe the Huskies have lost five in a row."

Kenny: "When sorrows come, they come not single spies, but in battalions." (Hamlet, Act 4, Scene 5)

Luke: "I hope our math test tomorrow isn't too hard."

Kenny: "Hope riseth like the sun in the east, shining on both the worthy and the less." (Made up.)

In the fall of 1964, thanks to fate and the alphabet, Carew, Cateere, and Daisy – Hoppy, me, and Luke – wound up side by side by side in the front row of Mr. Stokes' third grade class at Woodlake Elementary.

Scott Stokes had been a minor league pitcher in the late 50's before a torn rotator cuff sidelined his big league dreams and led him to a career in education. He grew up in Philadelphia, but his last baseball stop was in Tacoma with the Giants' AAA farm club. Like so many others, he fell in love with the Pacific Northwest and decided to stay.

Baseball's loss was our gain. He loved teaching, and we loved him. It didn't hurt that he brought his love for baseball with him. So when it was World Series time (the games were played in the daytime back then), he brought a TV into the classroom for us to watch. ("And learn," he said, maybe trying to convince himself as well as us.)

"Boys and girls," he told us, "hate can be a very bad thing. Very destructive, very damaging. You must be very careful what you decide to hate.

"I can only think of four things that are truly worthy of hate," he continued. "Nazis, Communism, Brussel Sprouts, and, maybe most of all, the New York Yankees."

And so it was that, in October of 1964, 24 eight- and nine-year-olds in Bonney Flats, Washington became big fans of the St.

Louis Cardinals. (Remember, we didn't have a Major League team of our own.) We all cheered wildly along with Mr. Stokes as those guys in the red uniforms, led by the great Bob Gibson, defeated the evil Yankees in a thrilling seven-game series.

Mr. Stokes was quick to recognize Luke's incredible athletic ability, and offered to coach and mentor him as much as the Daisys wanted. At their first parent-teacher conference he told Luke's parents, "I never made it to the big leagues myself, but I've got a good feeling that I'll be telling people I taught someone who did."

When I heard that, I remember thinking: "Yeah, unless he picks football or basketball." We all knew Luke would be a pro in one of the three sports. It was just a matter of which one.

Chapter 12

The Earth Moves

"Though the mountains be shaken and the hills be removed, yet my unfailing love for you will not be shaken, nor my covenant of peace be removed, says the Lord, who has compassion on you."
Isaiah 54:10

In the spring of 1971 Carole King sang *"I feel the earth move under my feet,"* but six years earlier, in the spring of 1965 we felt the earth move big time under our feet.

It was a Thursday morning, April 29, school had just started for the day and we were all pretty excited because we were headed on a field trip to the Seattle Opera House to see Rossini's *The Barber of Seville*. Not that we were really into opera, but Mrs. Daisy had been playing some of Mozart's music related to it, telling us what a cool story it was, and Mr. Daisy had been walking around the house singing, "Figaro, Figaro, Figaro" in his booming, slightly-off-key voice. So we were intrigued. Mostly, we just liked the idea of going to Seattle and missing a real day of school.

And then the rumbling started. The room shook, chairs fell over, books dropped off of shelves, the lights flickered, and some children screamed. I don't think I cried out, but I know I stood there not knowing what to do. Luke grabbed my arm and said, "Mouse, get under the desk." Then Mr. Stokes was telling all the kids to get under their desks.

The earthquake, which we found out later measured as high as 6.7 on a seismic scale, lasted for close to a minute (although it seemed much longer). It was long enough to really think: "How much is this desk gonna help me if the roof caves in?" When the rumbling stopped Mr. Stokes began to check that everyone was okay, and get a head count to make sure we were all accounted for. Three girls – Amanda Pruett, Janey Walker, and Jennifer Poe – had run outside, but they were soon rounded up and brought back inside. (Later I remember thinking they were probably the smartest, because a roof wouldn't fall on you if you were out in an open field.)

The only person missing was Ken Carew.

"Does anyone know where Kenny is?" Mr. Stokes asked with much concern.

"I think he went to the bathroom," Luke answered.

That's when the classroom door opened and Kenny stood there wide-eyed with a bemused look on his face.

"All right," he said. "Who's the wise guy who shook the bathroom while I was in there? I hit everything except the toilet. Somebody's got a real mess to clean up in there."

School was cancelled, and closed again the next day, and the field trip buses took us home instead of to Seattle. Woodlake Elementary suffered no structural damage, and Bonney Flats escaped the earthquake without significant loss, but overall in the region there was about $12 million in damages and seven deaths attributed to the quake.

That Sunday in church Mr. Daisy spoke from Isaiah 54: "Though the mountains be shaken and the hills be removed, yet my unfailing love for you will not be shaken, nor my covenant of peace be removed, says the Lord, who has compassion on you."

Still, people were pretty shook up, and we overheard some of the adults saying things like "end of times," "final days," and "coming tribulation." After all, the previous March, ironically on Good Friday, Alaska had experienced a massive earthquake, 9.2 on the Richter Scale lasting over 4 minutes.

"Dad," Luke asked. "Is the world about to end?" People are saying this is another sign that we are in the final days."

Mr. Daisy put his arm around both of us and did what he often did: reassure us with words from the Bible. "Boys," he said. "Jesus said in the book of Acts, 'It is not for you to know the times and dates the Father has set by His own authority.' Anybody who says they know is just plain wrong.

"Nobody knows when the end will come, for the whole world or for each of us individually," he continued. "It's certainly nothing to spend any time worrying about. Just live so that you make each day count, and plan to be here a long, long time."

There were several times in the next 10 years when I thought about those prophetic seven words Mr. Daisy said to us that day: "nobody knows when the end will come."

Chapter 13

Music and Movies

"Without music, life is a journey through the desert." – Pat Conroy

I know there are probably people from other generations who feel as though their music was the best. Those people are wrong! The music of the 60s and early 70s was the absolute greatest. "Indubitably and unequivocally," Kenny would say.

The soundtrack of our lives included the Beatles, Beach Boys, Rolling Stones, Herman's Hermits (Luke's favorite), Four Seasons, Turtles, Lovin' Spoonful (Kenny's favorite), Monkees, Hollies, Grass Roots (my favorite), Three Dog Night, Neil Diamond, and at least 50 more awesome groups and duos and solo artists. Thanks to Luke's older brothers and Kenny's older sisters, we had access to all the albums and singles we could ever hope to listen to, often in our rooms using pens or pencils as fake microphones to sing along and imagine being on big stages in front of huge crowds.

Mr. Daisy wasn't completely sure about the whole rock & roll craze – some of the people in his congregation were sure it was "of the devil" and wouldn't dream of letting their children listen to it. I think Mrs. Daisy helped convince him it was okay.

"Scott," she said. "this music is wonderful. The harmonies are magnificent. And listen to the words. Mostly it's about love. And don't forget: our parents hated our music, and these kids will probably grow up and hate their kids' music."

Mr. Daisy agreed, but warned us to be aware of the lyrics we were singing and make sure they weren't inappropriate. I don't think he ever became a huge rock & roll fan, but there were plenty of times I walked past his study and heard him humming something that sounded a lot like *"I want to hold your hand"* or *"She loves you, yeah, yeah, yeah."*

We were also entertained by Kenny, who could sound remarkably like the record we were listening to. When he sang "Mrs. Brown you've got a lovely daughter," you would have sworn he was part of the British invasion. Sometimes he would sing in his own voice, and we would think, "I hope he gives us front row tickets when he's a big star."

When Frankie Valli sang "walk like a man" in his falsetto, Kenny would say, "Yeah, why don't you sing like a man?!"

When Carly Simon sang "you're so vain, you probably think this song is about you," Kenny pointed out that "the song IS about him. He's not vain, he's smart. The title should be, *'You're so perceptive.'* "

Kenny also mixed up a lot of lyrics, sometimes intentionally, sometimes because he didn't know the real words.

So Creedence Clearwater's *"there's a bad moon on the rise"* became *"there's a bathroom on the right."*

Steppenwolf's *"get your motor running"* became *"ketchup warm and runny."*

Dylan's *"the answer my friends"* became *"the ants are my friends."*

The Fifth Dimension's *"age of aquarius"* became *"age of asparagus."*

And (one I'm pretty sure he did on purpose) when the Monkees sang *"then I saw her face, now I'm a believer,"* Kenny sang *"then I saw her face, now I'm gonna leave her."*

Some of the best music of our time came from the movies. The 60's were filled with great musicals – *Camelot, My Fair Lady, Mary Poppins, The Music Man, Oliver,* and, the greatest movie of all time, *The Sound of Music.* And thanks to Mrs. Daisy, we had the movie soundtrack albums of all of them. Luke and Kenny and I would even have yodeling contests while listening to "The Lonely Goatherd" from *The Sound of Music.*

In fact, *The Sound of Music* was the first movie our folks took us to. It was late May of 1965, not long after the earthquake, and most of our three families headed to the big screen Cinerama in downtown Seattle for a Friday night showing. What a wonderful night it was, even though we kids never liked having to wear a tie (remember, things were a lot different in those days). I think my dad had a little crush on Julie Andrews, Mrs. Daisy looked like she had died and gone to heaven, and Luke and I really came to understand why Mr. Stokes had told us it was okay to hate Nazis. Kenny's takeaway was that he hoped his dad wouldn't get the bright idea to use a whistle to round up all the Carew kids.

A couple of years later, in the summer of '67, we headed back to the same theatre in Seattle to watch the World War II classic *The Dirty Dozen.* More evil Nazis. Our parents had gone out somewhere together, and Matthew Daisy, who was home on leave between his two Vietnam tours, decided to take Luke and Kenny and me with him to a movie that I doubt our parents wanted us to see. It had a lot of violence and a lot of bad language, but like many other movies of that time, it was unrated. Which meant three 11-year-olds could walk right in with a 25-year-old adult, four people who believed the important truth that it is easier to get forgiveness than permission.

This movie had an all-star cast, including Lee Marvin, Donald Sutherland, and Charles Bronson. Just about every tough-guy actor of the time. But the real attraction, especially for Luke, was the appearance of Jimmy Brown, the greatest running back in the history of the NFL. In fact, the Cleveland Brown star announced his retirement from football, at the tender age of 29, during the filming of *The Dirty Dozen*.

Well, during the movie's climactic final battle scene, Brown's character, Robert T. Jefferson, is running through the Nazi compound throwing hand grenades into the open ventilation shafts of the Germans' bomb shelter when a Nazi machine gunner plugs him with about a thousand bullets and he stumbles to his death.

In that Seattle theatre, one viewer overcome with adrenaline, jumped up and hollered, "Man, that's the ONLY way to stop Jimmy!!"

True story.

Later that year Kenny, Luke, and I sat down to write our own best seller, a *completely unrelated* story about American soldiers who help win the war by breaking into a Nazi compound to kill several important German generals. Mrs. Carew typed it up for us, all 12 thrilling pages. It was called *The Gallant Five,* and like I said, was not any sort of rip-off of *The Dirty Dozen*. I'm sure it still stands as one of the greatest "novels" ever written by a trio of sixth graders.

Chapter 14

<u>Soccer</u>

"The great thing about team sports is that your joy in winning is multiplied and your pain in losing is divided." – Anonymous

In September of 1965 we started fourth grade at Woodlake Elementary, and the best thing about fourth grade in Bonney Flats was that we were finally old enough to play organized sports. The soccer craze in the Pacific Northwest was very new – it would grow to epic proportions – and the Bonney Flats Soccer Association was just in its third year. There were four age groups, and the youngest was for 10 & under – that was us!

There were eight teams in the league, all sponsored by local businesses. Luke, Hoppy, and I played for Wimpy's, the popular pizza place just a block away from Paul Revere High School – go Minutemen! Wimpy, the owner, was actually Fred Wimpleton, a large, good-natured fellow who loved, in order, pizza, sports, and children. Mr. Wimpleton and my mom went to school together and she told me that he got teased a lot by the class bullies, called *Wimpleton the Simpleton*. He just laughed, grew up to become a successful business owner, and loved taking the money from his former tormentors. Years later he told me that he had forgiven those boys, but "God forgive me, I do give them less toppings than I do for others," he said with a sheepish grin.

The best part about being sponsored by Wimpy's was free pizza for the whole team after every game. It sure beat playing for Nelson Dentistry, although Hoppy pointed out that it was a shame Mr. Wimpleton didn't own a motorcycle dealership.

In each of the four age groups (10 & under, 12 & under, 14 & under, 16 & under) there was a team sponsored by Junkers Realty, and Mr. Junkers took his sponsorship very seriously. He actively recruited the biggest and best athletes from around Bonney Flats to play on his teams, and his office was filled with all kinds of trophies and plaques from the soccer, baseball, basketball, and football teams he sponsored. I guess he wanted to show everybody what a winner he was, but my dad always thought it was strange how a grown man could become so invested in the wins and losses of children. Adults are strange sometimes.

Mr. Junkers did not approach the Daisys about Luke playing for his team. Dad explained that Mr. Junkers held too much animosity towards Mr. Daisy, and even if he had tried, there's no way Mr. Daisy would have let Luke go in that direction.

So here we were, a bunch of mostly 9-year-olds, playing against mostly 10-year-olds, many of whom had already played a year. We were almost always outside playing games, and as a group we were pretty athletic, but we rarely kicked around a soccer ball. In fact the closest thing we had was a red, rubber, sort of lopsided playground ball, until Mr. Carew bought us an official ball a month before our first practice.

What we did have was a great coach. His name was Dallas Chestnut, and he was from Liverpool. How a man from Liverpool came to be named Dallas was kind of a mystery, and he was sure to tell anyone who asked (which was everyone), that, no, he had never met the Beatles.

Coach Chestnut had been playing soccer "pretty much all of my 35 years," and loved teaching us the rules and the skills and the strategy of the game. His son Austin (again with the hard-to-explain Texas thing) was one of the few 10-year-olds on the team. Austin was very skinny, very slow afoot, suffered from allergies that left him with a perpetual runny nose, and was quite clearly absent the day God was handing out athletic ability. But he tried as hard as anyone, and we all loved him. Coach Chestnut was not blind to his son's soccer shortcomings, and just wanted him to learn the game, grow to love it, and build friendships with boys who would be kind to him. It worked.

So we had a great coach and boys who loved to play and compete, but mostly, we had Luke. From the very start of our very first game, he dominated. He would score 5 or 6 goals in the first half of most every game, and then, if we had a big lead, Mr. Daisy would look at Luke and kind of shake his head as if to say, "That's enough." Luke would then spend the rest of the game passing the ball, hoping to let some of the rest of us score.

At halftime of our first game, which we won 9-2 over Jerry's Chevron, several of the other team's parents came over complaining about Luke and how he must be too old for this division. Mrs. Daisy began carrying Luke's birth certificate in her purse to head off the complaints.

We kept winning, and we kept getting better. Hoppy was still small, but very fast, and he became a pretty good goal-scorer in his own right. And maybe some of Luke's incredible ability to anticipate began to wear off on me, because I became a pretty good goaltender.

The greatest moment of the season came in our next-to-last game. We were playing Norgaard Pharmacy in a driving rainstorm, leading just 2-0 as halftime approached. Luke stole a pass at midfield and fed it to Hoppy on the wing, who dribbled down the left sideline and centered it back to Luke.

Luke planted his right foot and swept his left leg back for a booming kick which we had seen hit the back of the net so many times. But this time his plant foot slipped in the mud and the ball went high, ricocheting off the crossbar as the goalie dived to his right to try to make the stop.

The ball caromed out about 12 yards, and right there waiting, runny nose and all, was Austin Chestnut. He leaped forward and headed the ball, just like his dad had taught him, right into the corner of the net.

We all went crazy, and pretty soon it was a muddy pig pile on Austin. Coach Chestnut had tears in his eyes when dad and Mr. Daisy patted him on the back. Luke said he had never been so happy to slip and fall. And later Austin, with a mouthful of Wimpy's pepperoni pizza, said, "It was pretty cool ... until you guys tried to kill me in the mud."

Wouldn't you know, the last game of the season was against Junkers Realty, and both teams were undefeated. They were mostly bigger and older, and they had some very good players. But they didn't have Luke.

Over the years I saw Luke play at three different levels:

1. Great!
2. Amazing!!

and 3. "Holy cow did you see that? I can't believe what he just did!!!"

On this particular Saturday afternoon he played at level 3 and we won, 5-1. Luke scored five goals. I made a couple of my best saves of the year, but lost the shutout when their best player, Tom Egbert, scored on a corner kick in the final minute.

Mr. Junkers was on the sideline, screaming at the poor teenage referee just about the whole game, turning more and more red as the game wore on. At one point, my dad walked over and tried to calm him down.

"Come on, Jack," he said. "It's just a kids' game, and it's a kid refereeing. For crying out loud, you're going to have a heart attack."

Even Mrs. Junkers, who rarely crossed her belligerent husband, was fed up. "Jack, you're embarrassing us all," she said.

None of it worked. Mr. Junkers continued to berate the ref, then his own coach and players, and finally said some derogatory things about us.

When it was over and all the hands had been shook and the post-game orange slices had been devoured, Coach Chestnut did what he always did, asked each of us for a comment about the game.

Hoppy was the first to raise his hand, and looking a little sad, offered, "I feel bad that I didn't get a chance to tell Mr. Junkers something."

"What's that, Kenny?" Coach Chestnut asked.

Then smiling and bopping in his best Ray Charles, Hoppy sang, "Hit the road, Jack. And don't you come back no more no more no more no more. Hit the road, Jack. And don't you come back no more."

This time it was wild, crazy pig pile on Kenny.

When the season ended all of our Bonney Flats teams headed up to Vancouver, British Columbia on Thanksgiving weekend to play three games against the Canadian teams in our own age group. What an eye opener!

Luke was still the best player on the field in every game, but these kids had been playing since they were old enough to walk, and we lost all three games. They would have two players marking Luke wherever he was on the field, sometimes three. He still scored a goal or two every game, but it wasn't enough. I think maybe it was the only time he ever lost consecutive games in any sport.

On our trip home I asked him if he thought soccer might be his new favorite sport.

"Nah," he said. "I think maybe this is it for me in soccer."

"Really? How come?" I was kind of shocked.

"Well, I love the running and the teamwork," he explained. "But it just doesn't feel like a real sport if you can't use your hands. I think we were meant to use our hands. Why else would God have given them to us?"

"I get to use my hands as the goalie," I countered.

"Maybe Luke's right," Hoppy interjected. "Maybe if God had intended for us to be soccer players, only 1 out of every 11 babies born would have hands. And their parents would be so excited they'd say, 'Oh look! It's a goalie!' "

Chapter 15

TV Shows and Battleship

"We owe a lot to Thomas Edison. If it weren't for him, we'd all be watching television by candlelight." – Milton Berle

The decade of the 60's was a pretty amazing time to grow up. I was too young to remember the Bay of Pigs (April, 1961) or the Cuban missile crisis (October, 1962), but I remember very clearly the three assassinations. I have less vivid recollections of the race riots – we didn't really have any here in the Pacific Northwest – and our interest in Vietnam was centered more around Matthew Daisy's experiences than the war protests that kept building as the decade wound down.

That stuff was all in the real world. In kid world we had other important things to worry about. Like: would Gilligan ever get off that island? And as Hoppy would point out: with Ginger and Mary Ann there, why would he want to?

We loved to joke about all the absurdities of Gilligan's Island:

1. Why did Mr. Howell bring a chest full of cash for a 3-hour tour?
2. Why did Ginger wear a formal dress and high heels on a boat?
3. How could they get radio reception if they were 400 miles from civilization?
4. If the professor was so smart, how come he kept putting Gilligan in charge of their rescue?

None of it made sense. We watched every episode. Several times.

So while it's true that we grew up with the best music, to be honest, we really had the goofiest television shows. We were asked to believe in a horse that could talk *(Mr. Ed)* a woman who was reincarnated into an automobile (*My Mother the Car*), and a nun who could fly (*The Flying Nun*, of course). There was a woman who could make anything appear or disappear by twitching her nose (*Bewitched*), and another who could make anything appear or disappear by folding her arms and blinking (*I Dream of Jeannie*). And both of those women had men who refused to let them conjure up a million dollars. What were they thinking? There was a family of friendly monsters (*The Munsters*), and another of benevolent ghouls (*The Addams Family*). There was an alien who had TV antennas coming out of the back of his head, but nobody knew he was an alien (*My Favorite Martian*). And for the more serious-minded, a dolphin who could foil criminal plots (*Flipper*).

So silly. But of course, we knew every theme song.

We did have some very educational Saturday morning cartoons, however. (Back in those days cartoons could only be seen on Saturdays.) We learned, among other things, that some ghosts were friendly (*Casper*), a can of spinach could help you defeat any enemy (*Popeye*), and *Acme* products were not effective in fighting annoying desert birds (*Roadrunner*).

One of our favorite after-school fares, when it was too cold or rainy to be playing outside, was *The Adventures of Superman*, reruns from the original TV series that first aired in the 50's with George Reeves as the man of steel.

"Isn't it weird?" Hoppy observed after one episode (I'm not sure which one, but they were all pretty much the same). "When Superman flies into the room with the crooks, he stands there with his hands on his hips while they shoot at him, all of their bullets bouncing off his chest. But then when they run out of bullets, they throw their guns at him, AND HE DUCKS. What's that about? It's like he's saying, 'Your puny human weapons cannot harm me and I will ... WHOA ... you almost hit me with that gun.' I don't get it."

And when I say *we* watched every episode of all those silly shows, I'm talking about Hoppy, Johnny, and me. Luke didn't have time to sit and watch TV. He was either out shooting baskets, both left- and right-handed. Or finding someone to pitch balls to him (baseballs, whiffle balls, tennis balls). Or playing street football with the older kids. You might say he was a tad bit obsessed with sports.

But in the Pacific Northwest, you may have heard, outdoor sporting activities are often cancelled or postponed because of a little thing called rain. Somebody once said it only rains once a year in the Seattle area – November through May. Hoppy used to say that "we have 350 days of clear skies and sunshine .... but that's over a five-year period."

There were a lot of Friday nights when we had trouble sleeping, too eager to find out if our Saturday baseball games were going to be played or rained out. When the rain won out, we often alleviated our disappointment by having some kind of an indoor game tournament.

One time, I remember, we had reached the title match of the Bonney Flats *Battleship* Championships, Luke vs. Hoppy. *Battleship* is a game where you place your five ships on a board, hidden from your opponent, who then calls out coordinates to try to locate your ships and destroy your fleet.

Early in the championship match Hoppy threw his arms up in triumph and yelled, "I won!"

"What do you mean you won?" Luke asked.

"I won!" Hoppy repeated.

"You didn't win," Luke said a little testy. "Now shut up and play."

"I won!" Hoppy said again.

Now Luke was visibly angry. "Stop saying that or I'm gonna come over there and thump you," he said, tight-lipped. (Even though we all knew Luke would never physically thump any of us.)

Finally Hoppy started laughing.

"No," he explained. "That's my guess. The coordinate I – 1. I'm guessing I – 1."

We all laughed. Even Luke. It was about the only time anybody got under his skin.

Play resumed. Luke won.

"Hey Hoppy," he said. "Guess what."

Kenny nodded knowingly. "Yeah, yeah. I know."

Chapter 16

Track Meet

"Those who hope in the Lord will renew their strength. They will soar on wings like eagles. They will run and not grow weary." – Isaiah 40:31

Every year in early spring the Bonney Flats School District held a district-wide elementary school track meet for fourth, fifth, and sixth graders. And it was a pretty big deal. The competition was held at one of the high schools, odd years at Paul Revere and even years at Madison, and always drew a great crowd. Cheerleaders from both high schools and the four junior highs would come and cheer, local businesses put together a program with the names of all the competitors, and the weekly newspaper, *The Bonney Flats Courier-Herald,* would post pictures of all the winners.

Each of the eight grade schools would have their own qualifying meet and then send their boy and girl representatives from each of the three grades in five events: the 100-yard dash, 440-yard run, one mile run, long jump, and softball throw. For Woodlake Elementary School fourth graders, Luke would have won all five events, but you were only allowed to compete in one. So he asked Hoppy and me which events we thought we had our best chances in. Hoppy picked the 100-yard dash and I chose the mile, so Luke settled on the 440-yard run (there was no silly talk of switching to the metric system back in those days). We each won our event at school and got to advance to the big district-wide meet.

So there we were, the three of us fourth graders in our navy blue Woodlake Royals t-shirts, ready to run on an unusually warm and sunny spring Saturday afternoon in the South Puget Sound area.

It was April of 1966, we were 10 years old, and up to that point our interaction with, and interest in, girls was at a bare minimum. Mostly we just ignored them, unless we were trying to figure out what all the giggling was about, or running away when one of them decided to chase us at recess. Some of Kenny's older sisters seemed pretty cool, but the younger ones were kind of annoying and acted like we were something stuck to the bottom of their shoes.

But that day it changed. At least it did for me.

She had long blonde hair in a pony tail that swung back and forth when she ran, bright green eyes and a smile as wide as the ocean. There was a scar that started just under her left eye and carried almost all the way to her mouth. She never stopped smiling or bouncing around, and was surrounded by the rest of her classmates like she was a magnet. I couldn't stop staring at her.

"Mouse," Luke yelled, startling me out of my reverie.

"What?" I answered, coming out of my daze.

"What's the matter with you?" he asked. "That's the third time I've called out to you."

"It's that girl over there," I said, pointing. "Do you know who she is?"

"Nope. But I'll go find out."

A few minutes later he came back. "She's a fourth grader at Morgan Elementary," he explained. "Her name's Ellie. Ellie Fent. I guess she's running the 440 for them. They say she's really fast."

We had heard the Fent name before. She had a couple of older brothers who were troublemakers. "Hoods" we called them. The kind of kids that got suspended from school for smoking or swearing or fighting, who usually turned out to be petty thugs and not hardened criminals. At least that was the hope. This shining light of a girl didn't seem like she could be a part of the same family.

Hoppy was the first of us to run, and he did great, finishing in second place, just a hair behind Craig Smith of Blythe McCormick Elementary.

When the gun sounded to start the fourth grade girls' 440-yard run, I watched as Ellie took off like a shot and won the race by about 30 yards, smiling the whole way. She was amazing!

The next race was the fourth grade boys' 440-yard run, and it was pretty much an exact replica of the girls' race. This time it was Luke who looked like he was shot out of a cannon and won by about the same margin.

When it was time for my race, every thought about pace and strategy and running form had fled from my head like leaves in a hurricane. All I could think was: "I'm gonna win this race so easily, and she's going to watch me and be so impressed, and then she'll come over and congratulate me and smile at me, right at me, and I'll think of something clever to say and she will laugh, and then we'll stand next to each other when we get our medals." Nothing was going to stop me.

The starting gun sounded and I took off like I was on fire. Halfway around the first lap I was so far ahead I would have needed binoculars to see the next closest runner. This was going to be so easy.

The crowd was cheering and I stole a look into the infield to see if she was watching. Instead I saw Luke, running towards me and yelling something.

"Slow down, Mouse. Slow down!" he screamed.

Slow down? Why on earth would I slow down and postpone my glory?

And then it happened. As I finished the first lap, about 100 yards in front, a bear jumped on my back. Okay, not a real bear, but it sure felt like it. Halfway around lap 2, the second place guy had already caught and passed me. As I finished the second lap, the bear on my back picked up a piano. Halfway through lap 3 all the other runners had passed me and a hippo sat on the piano on the bear on my back.

Could I muster up the strength to make a final charge and pull out a miraculous comeback that would earn me all those things I had been hoping for? I took stock of my resources:

Legs: burning

Lungs: aching

Back: throbbing

Head: pounding

Will to live: evaporating

There would be no comeback, although I am proud to say I finished the third lap just before the other runners completed the race, so I didn't get lapped. But now there was one more lap to run, a lap of shame, with nobody else left on the track. I decided to give up.

"Don't quit," Luke said, right there next to me on the infield. "DO NOT QUIT, Mouse! Let's finish this together."

I looked into my friend's eyes and could see how much it meant to him that I keep going. So I nodded slowly and started to trudge again.

"Come on. Here we go," he urged.

He ran next to me and kept encouraging me. "Deep, slow breaths. Use your arms. Try to lengthen your stride."

Halfway down the backstretch a funny thing happened. The hippo jumped off the piano. Then the piano slipped off the bear. And finally, as I hit the home stretch, the bear jumped off. I realized the fans were cheering for me – last place me. I felt my muscles reawaken and I crossed that finish line with a surge of power and speed.

"Good job," Luke said, arm around my shoulder. "I'm real proud of you, Mouse."

Bent over, hands on my knees, I managed to answer. "Thanks, Luke. I needed your help."

"You know what," he answered. "That's what brothers do."

Somebody handed me a towel and some water, and after a few minutes I realized I was probably not going to die.

"Hey," somebody said to me from behind. I turned around, and it was her. It was Ellie. "That was pretty cool the way you didn't give up and kept on running. I liked that."

Now was the time to say something clever. Be cool, Michael.

"Shucks, it tweren't nothin', ma'am."

or

"I normally don't give out autographs, but if you insist."

or

"The name's Cateere. Michael Cateere."

Instead what came out of me was this: "Uhhhhhhhhhhh."

"Anyway," she said, turning to leave. "I just wanted to say nice going."

And so I watched her bounce away, joining her group of friends.

"Wow!" Luke said. "That was really smooth, Mouse. You sounded just like Clint Eastwood."

"Shut up, Luke."

I don't know what my final mile time was – they didn't time the last place finishers – but Kenny was kind enough to point out that it appeared they timed me with a calendar. There were 2 district records set that day: the 4th grade girls 440-yard run, Ellie Fent; and the 4th grade boys 440-yard run, Luke Daisy. So after all the events were completed, somebody had the idea to have Luke and Ellie race against each other.

I could tell Luke did not like the idea, but with everybody forcing the issue, he agreed. So they raced another 440-yard run. And Ellie won. Luke never admitted that he didn't try his hardest, but his time was much slower than his first race. I always felt like he did it for me. Years later Ellie told me she thought he did it for her.

As we headed out to the parking lot we heard an unmistakable sneering voice coming up from behind us.

"Hey Puke Pansy." It was the bully Bruce Junkers, who had won the 6th grade 440-yard run that day. "I heard you got beat by a girl."

We stopped and turned to face him. Our parents were there with us, so Junkers knew there wouldn't be a fight. Still, I had to wonder how somebody whose legs moved so fast could have a brain that moved so slowly. And Johnny, who was holding Luke's hand, could feel his twin brother tense up.

"Dohna hurhim, Wookie," he said, just as he had 3 ½ years earlier when we first encountered this menace.

"What do you want, son?" Mr. Daisy asked him calmly.

"I'm not your son," Bruce said derisively.

"I think I know what he wants," I chimed in. "I think he wants to race Luke himself. Isn't that right, Bruce? You want to race Luke who got beat by a girl. I think that's a great idea."

Bruce just looked at me like he wanted to kill me. Finally, not really knowing how to back down, he said, "Yeah, okay. I'll race you."

They lined up, somebody yelled go, and off they ran. It was actually pretty close – for about 50 yards. And then Luke began to pull away. By the time they hit the far turn the only question was how much Luke would win by. But we didn't find out because Junkers did the only thing he could think of to try and save face: he grabbed his leg and pulled up limping. Then he hobbled away.

Luke 2, Bully 0. Not that I was keeping score.

Chapter 17

Little League

"Little League baseball is a very good thing because it keeps the parents off the streets." – Yogi Berra

In the late spring of 1966 we played in our first Little League season. Almost all of us 10-year-olds, including Hoppy and me, made the Minors. Not only was Luke chosen for the Majors, playing against 11- and 12-year-olds, but he was one of the 2 or 3 best players in the league and was selected for the Bonney Flats All-Star team.

The rest of the world was about to get its first glimpse of Luke Daisy.

The All-Star team was selected and coached by the manager of the team that won the league championship. In 1966 the championship was won by JJ's Auto Dealership, and the coach of JJ's Auto Dealership was a man by the name of Frank Jones.

Mr. Jones was a hard-nosed, no-nonsense, former drill sergeant who was the General Manager of JJ's Auto Dealership, which meant he worked for Mr. Junkers. Mr. Jones told my dad that Junkers had instructed him not to select Luke for the All-Star team.

"If you pick the Daisy kid for the team," Mr. Junkers had told him, "don't bother showing up for work on Monday, because you won't have a job."

"I think that's very interesting," Mr. Jones responded. "And you know who else would find that very interesting? My older brother, the attorney, and my younger brother, the newspaper editor."

Luke was chosen for the team and Mr. Jones continued to run JJ's Auto Dealership.

Of course this meant that Luke and the bully Bruce Junkers would be teammates, since Bruce was one of the best pitchers in the league. Unfortunately – or fortunately, depending on how you look at it – Bruce broke his hand in a mini-bike accident the week of all-star tryouts and had to be left off the team.

Why a sixth grader was given his own mini-bike to ride – in this case an Arctic-Cat with a 4.5 horsepower engine that could go over 25 MPH – was kind of a mystery. When word got around that he had crashed it into a tree and broken his hand, it kept the rest of us from even trying to nag our parents into buying one for us.

Losing Bruce Junkers might have hurt the team's chances of winning tournaments, but nobody seemed too upset about it. They still had two great pitchers – a tall right-hander named Mike Monroe who threw flaming fastballs, and a left-hander named William Botts who threw sidearm and was one of the first kids we knew who could throw a really great curveball. Both were headed into seventh grade, as was the rest of the team, except for one other boy who was going to be a sixth grader, and Luke, who would be in fifth grade in the fall. Luke may have been the youngest on the team, but he was one of the tallest, and most certainly the strongest. His mom still carried his birth certificate to every game.

Luke played shortstop and batted leadoff. I don't know if he was the only Little League switch hitter in the country that year, but he was the only one that I ever saw. It became a family affair when they named my dad as team doctor/trainer, and I got to be the bat boy/equipment manager/water boy. I didn't get a uniform, but I did get to sit in the dugout and have my own B.F.A.S. baseball cap (Bonney Flats All-Star). And the best part was I got to go to every game.

The district tournament was held at Sick's Stadium in Seattle the final weekend of July, and the eight-team, single elimination tournament included, in addition to Bonney Flats, teams from Bellingham, Mount Vernon, Everett, Seattle, Renton, Kent, and Auburn.

Sick's Stadium had been built in 1938 by a man named Emil Sick, and was home to Seattle's minor league baseball team. Sick, who also owned the Rainier Brewing Company, built his cozy little ballpark in a part of Seattle called the Rainier Valley, with a beautiful view of Mount Rainier, and named his team - you guessed it - the Rainiers.

When he died in 1964 ownership of the stadium was split between several family members, so the name was changed to Sicks' Stadium. Changing a stadium's name by simply moving the apostrophe one letter to the right seemed like one of Kenny's favorite Shakespeare plays, *"Much Ado About Nothing."* But it was an excellent lesson in correct punctuation for plural versus singular nouns.

In 1965 the Rainiers were sold from the Boston Red Sox to the Los Angeles Angels, and Sicks' Stadium became the home to the Class AAA Angels. It was as close as we got to the big leagues until the American League expanded and added the Seattle Pilots for the 1969 season. That little experiment lasted just one year before the league stole our team and moved them to Milwaukee. I guess they didn't like the idea of playing in a stadium that held just over 17,000 fans and would run out of water pressure by the seventh inning.

 So even though it wasn't a major league park at the time, we were very excited to play on the same field as a bunch of guys who had made it to the big leagues: base-stealing wizard Maury Wills; Hall of Famer Bob Lemon; and a couple of guys with the coolest names, Rico Petrocelli and Vada Pinson.

The fences at Sicks' were just over 300 feet in left and right fields, so the tournament officials built temporary fences to reasonable Little League dimensions, 210 feet all around. The Angels were playing on the road that week, so the stadium could easily be put back to normal before their next home stand.

Our first game was against Bellingham and our guys seemed very nervous. In the top of the first inning our leftfielder misjudged a fly ball, our first baseman dropped a throw right to him, and suddenly we were behind 2-0.

"All right, men," Coach Jones said as the team reached the dugout. Even though it was a bunch of 10-, 11-, and 12-year-olds, he always called us men. "Enough of that nonsense. Now, Luke, get us started."

And he did. Luke hit the first pitch way over the leftfield fence for a leadoff home run. And he ran around the bases without so much as a smile, let alone jumping up and down. I think he wanted to show the rest of the guys that we just needed to calm down and play with some quiet confidence.

And we did. Everybody got hits, Luke added a couple of doubles, and we won our first game easily, 9-3.

We played Renton in the semifinals, and again we won easily, 7-0. Botts pitched a 2-hit shutout and struck out 12 batters in the six innings. I don't think their hitters had ever seen a real curve ball. Luke hit two home runs, one to left and one to center.

In the championship game we faced Seattle, and Luke didn't get a single hit. That's because they walked him intentionally all three times he batted, including once to lead off the game and once with runners on first and second.

We were leading 3-2 in the bottom of the sixth with two outs and a runner on first when their cleanup hitter hit a double into the gap in left center. Luke took the relay throw from our left fielder and fired a perfect strike to the catcher, who made the tag on their streaking runner for the final out of the game.

We were District champs and headed to the State tournament.

The state tournament was the next weekend in Wenatchee with the four district champions in a double-elimination format. We were matched against Spokane, Yakima, and Vancouver, three cities quite a bit larger than Bonney Flats. Again we won all three games (4-1, 5-1, and 6-1), and the boys from Bonney Flats were now State Champions.

In Luke's 10 plate appearances he had five hits, three walks, and he flew out twice. That's a .714 batting average, but it was his play in the field that had people shaking their heads. He caught one foul ball that bounced off the third baseman's glove, made one over-the-shoulder catch on a blooper hit to left field, and made a diving stop on a hard grounder hit up the middle, and from his stomach flipped it back-handed to the second baseman for the force out.

The Northwest Regional tournament includes the state champions from Washington, Oregon, Idaho, Montana, Wyoming, and Alaska. In 1966 the tournament was held in Eugene.

This time we had to battle back through the losers' bracket, which we did, and we faced a team from Fairbanks for the championship. Bottom of the sixth, score tied 3-3, Luke came to the plate with two outs and a runner on first. Their manager strolled to the mound to talk to the pitcher and decide whether or not to walk him.

You could tell that the manager wanted to walk Luke, but the pitcher, who was their star player and happened to be the coach's son, kept arguing that he didn't want to. You could pretty easily read his lips and his body language. "I can get him, dad," he was saying. "Trust me, I know I can get him out."

Finally the dad/manager nodded, patted his son/pitcher on the back and said, "Okay. Go get him, son." You kind of have to admire a man for having that kind of confidence in his son and trusting him in a big moment like that. I think he was probably a great dad.

Maybe not a great manager.

Luke hit the first pitch about 50 feet over the centerfield wall, we won the game 5-3, and the Bonney Flats all stars were headed to the Little League World Series.

Pandemonium ensued, with lots of whooping and hollering and hugging and back-slapping, right there at home plate. Finally things calmed down and we headed back into the dugout, exhausted.

"We did it," I exclaimed. "I can't believe it. We're going to the World Series."

"What do you mean 'we'," Mitch Templeton scoffed. Mitch was one of our outfielders, and one of the best friends of the bully Bruce Junkers. "You're not even on the team, Cateere. You're just the water boy."

I felt so humiliated, and I could feel my face heat up and turn red. The dugout fell silent and all I could do was look down at my feet, wishing I hadn't said anything.

"Yeah, right, Mitch," Luke spoke up, breaking the silence. "Tell us all now: how many hits do you have so far? We've played about a dozen games, and you have how many hits?" We all knew the answer.

"I think the number is zero," Luke continued. "So Mouse here has as many hits as you do. The difference is, he doesn't sit on the end of the bench and pout when he strikes out or gets taken out of the game."

It was the first, and only, time I ever saw Luke speak harshly to a teammate. I know he felt bad about it, but it was something he thought he had to do. If there was one thing Luke hated, it was bullies. Mitch just threw his helmet against the fence and stormed out.

"Thanks, Luke," I said, still feeling embarrassed.

"Hey," Luke answered. "That's what brothers do."

But he could see I was still upset.

"Listen, Mouse," he said. "Mitch is a jerk. Everybody else here is glad you're part of the team. When you said 'we', you were absolutely right." I felt much better when every other player on the team walked by and either slapped me on the back or shook my hand or scruffled my hair, adding kind words along the way.

Mitch did not make the trip to the World Series with us because he decided to quit the team and, in a great irony, told his dad it was because he was being bullied.

When Mr. Templeton came to talk to the coach about his son being bullied, Coach Jones handled it pretty well.

"I'll tell you what, Mr. Templeton," he said. "Let's ask the other boys on the team if they thought Mitch was being bullied, or if he was the bully. And then we can have them vote on whether or not they want Mitch back on the team. What do you think?"

Mr. Templeton nodded slowly and a sad look of understanding came into his eyes.

"I think I get the picture," he said. "I'll talk to my son. Thanks, coach."

That couldn't have been easy. He turned to leave but stopped and turned back. "Good luck in the world series," he added. "You guys have really made us all proud."

Chapter 18

Road Trip

"Good company in a journey makes the way seem shorter." –
Izaak Walton.

We had two weeks between the regional tournament and the
world series, so the Daisy and Cateere families hit the road from
Bonney Flats, Washington to Williamsport, Pennsylvania in our
brand new 1966 Ford Country Squire station wagon. This beige
beauty featured the simulated wood grain body paneling,
palomino interior, seat belts (standard option that year), 22-
gallon gas tank, three bench seats, one facing backwards, and a
swing-out, fold-down tailgate with a roll-down rear window. It
was powered by a 289 cubic-inch, V-8 engine with a 3-speed
automatic transmission. (I don't really know what any of that
means, but I saw it on the commercial and heard Matthew Daisy
talk about it.)

Dad drove with mom and Mrs. Daisy next to him in the front,
Mr. Daisy and Mark rode in the middle seat, and Luke, Johnny,
and I rode in the back, facing out the back window. It's almost
like you have a whole different vacation than the rest of the
passengers when you're facing the other direction. Luke and I
would play the alphabet game and the license plate game, and
Johnny would see how many people in passing cars he could get
to wave at him. (Folks in Montana were the friendliest.)

When our eyes got tired of searching for letters or looking at
license plates, Luke said, "Come on Mouse, you gotta think of a
game we can play."

"Okay," I said, after giving it a little thought. "Let's see who can name the most Beatles' songs."

"Yeah, count me in," Mark said excitedly.

"Me, too," Dad chimed in.

"We'll all play," Mrs. Daisy added. "We'll take turns naming one."

"Yeah, but if you can't think of one, or you say one that's already been said, you're out," I said.

"Okay, but one more rule," Mrs. Daisy said. "You have to sing your choice."

This was met with some groans, but in the end Mrs. Daisy prevailed. The good news was we got to hear her beautiful singing voice. But the bad news was we had to listen to Luke sing – the boy couldn't carry a tune in a bucket.

"Mouse, you go first since it was your idea," she said.

So I started with an easy one. "Can't buy me love. No, no, no, no," I sang.

Luke went next singing (trying to sing) "It's been a hard day's night, and I've been working like a dog."

We skipped Johnny because he was sleeping.

Mark jumped in with "Nowhere Man."

Mr. Daisy's turn, and he gave us a stirring rendition of "Good day sunshine." Those were the only words he knew, so he repeated them seven times. Now we were all laughing.

Mrs. Daisy then began to sing and we all listened quietly: "There were bells, on a hill, but I never heard them ringing. No I never heard them at all. 'Till there was you." Beautiful.

Mom hit us with "Got to get you into my life," and dad followed with an inspired version of "Paperback Writer."

Soon it was a giant sing-along, no longer a competition, just a station wagon full of friends and family enjoying the greatest musical group of all time. (There can be no debate about this!) Before you knew it we had twisted and shouted, travelled here, there, and everywhere with our ticket to ride all the way across the great state of Minnesota.

Suddenly Johnny hollered, "Help! Help!"

"What is it, Johnny?" Mr. Daisy turned around quickly to find out what was the matter. Johnny was terrified of spiders. "Is it a spider?"

"Help! Help!" Johnny said again.

Luke took his twin brother by the shoulders, which is the way he could always get Johnny's attention. "What is it, Johnny? Did you see something that scared you? Does somebody need our help?"

Then Johnny started to giggle, which took us all by surprise.

"Help," he explained. "That's my Beatles' song. I win."

I think we were halfway through Wisconsin before we stopped laughing.

It was a trip with a lifetime of memories as we hit all the main landmarks: Yellowstone, Little Big Horn, Mount Rushmore, Wrigley Field, Lake Michigan, the Football Hall of Fame in Canton, Ohio, and our favorite stop of all, the Baseball Hall of Fame in Cooperstown, New York (slightly out of the way). Of course dad, with his slightly warped sense of humor, also had to stop and see the world's largest toilet seat collection in Coeur d'Alene, Idaho, and the Museum of Dryer Lint Art in Eau Claire, Wisconsin.

What a stroke of fantastic timing luck to visit Cooperstown in August of 1966, because less than a month earlier the Hall of Fame had inducted two of its most acclaimed members: Charles "Casey" Stengel, and Theodore "Ted" Williams. Stengel was one of the most colorful characters in baseball history, and Williams was one of the two or three greatest hitters to ever play the game.

Casey Stengel managed the New York Yankees dynasty from 1949-1960, winning 10 pennants and 7 world championships, including 5 in a row from '49-'53. He once said that "the key to being a good manager is keeping the players who hate me away from those who are still undecided."

He had several other memorable lines, including:

"Line up alphabetically, according to your height."

"You have to have a catcher, or you'll wind up with a lot of passed balls."

After his stint with the Yankees, Stengel managed perhaps the worst team of all time, the expansion New York Mets, from '62-'65. That '62 team, which he famously nicknamed "The Amazin'

Mets," finished with 40 wins and 120 losses, which was 60 games behind the National League champion Giants.

"I've been in this game 100 years," he said of that team, "but I'm seeing ways to lose games that I never even knew existed."

Ted Williams, on the other hand, was not one to clown around. His incredible career with the Boston Red Sox, which included a career batting average of .344, 521 home runs, and two triple crowns, was interrupted by 3 years of military service during World War II and two years of service during the Korean War. He was commissioned a second lieutenant in the U.S. Marine Corps as a naval aviator.

Nicknamed "The Splendid Splinter," Williams was the last player to bat over .400 for a single season. In 1941, he went 6-for-8 in a doubleheader on the season's final day to finish at .406. Even now, almost 8 decades later, the closest anybody has come to that mark was the great Tony Gwynn, who batted .394 in 1994.

"If I'd have known hitting .400 was going to be such a big deal," Williams once said in a rare moment of levity, "I would have done it again."

And talk about going out in style: on September 28, 1960, in the final at bat of his career, Williams launched one over the right field wall in Boston's Fenway Park for a home run.

So there we were, Luke and me, a couple of 10-year-old baseball fanatics, reading all about Stengel and Williams, as well as other legends like Ruth, Gehrig, Cobb, and Dimaggio.

A thought occurred to me.

"You know what, Luke," I said. "Someday you'll be in here."

"Well of course, Mouse," he answered. "I'm already in here. We both are. Pay attention."

"No, you big goof," I laughed. "Someday you'll be inducted here."

Luke paused and thought it over for a few seconds. And then he nodded.

"Well, that would be pretty cool," he said.

Chapter 19

World Series

"Love is the most important thing in the world, but the World Series is pretty good, too." – Yogi Berra

Williamsport, Pennsylvania, population 40,000 in 1966, was the birthplace of Little League baseball, with the first games played there in 1939, and the World Series started there in 1947. So when the Bonney Flats All-Stars made its appearance, the area was celebrating the 20th Annual Little League World Series, which made it an even bigger deal than usual.

Williamsport sits in north central Pennsylvania, the county seat of Lycoming County. It is the cultural and financial center of the region, and it has a very interesting history. In the 30 years leading up to and through the Civil War, the underground railroad, used by escaping southern slaves seeking their freedom, operated in and around Williamsport. In the late 1800s it was called "The Lumber Capital of the World," and was said to have more millionaires per capita than any other city. In fact, the local high school took the name Millionaires as its team name. I'm not sure if the mascot was covered in dollar bills and credit cards, or how well that nickname went over with their opponents.

One of Williamsport's natives with a most interesting story was Joseph Lockard. As a 19-year-old Army private, he was stationed at Wheeler Army Airfield in Oahu. On the morning of December 7, 1941 he was one of two young soldiers manning the U.S. Army's SCR-270 radar at Opana Point near the island's northern tip. Shortly after 7 a.m. their radar screen went crazy, showing "something like I'd never seen before," he said. "I knew something wasn't right, but I just didn't know what."

So he called it in to his superior, who dismissed the radar sighting, believing it was a flight of American B-17 "Flying Fortress" bombers scheduled to arrive from the mainland.

It was not.

It was, instead, nearly 200 war planes of the Imperial Japanese Navy, the first wave of the attack on Pearl Harbor, which resulted in the deaths of over 2,300 U.S. servicemen, 18 warships sunk, and over 200 planes destroyed.

If Lockard's warning had been heeded, "it would not have prevented the attack," he always pointed out. But it would have given Pearl Harbor's defense forces a half-hour to prepare for it, and most certainly mitigate some of the damage. His is the story of a hero that might have been.

It was a great honor for us to have Joe Lockard, then a 44-year-old mechanical engineer, throw out the first pitch of the 1966 Little League World Series. It was especially meaningful for Mr. Daisy, who at the time of the attack was a 25-year-old pilot stationed at nearby Hickam Air Force Base. In the very early morning hours of December 7, Mrs. Daisy had delivered their oldest son, Matthew, and the three of them were in Tripler Military Medical Center in Honolulu when the attack on Pearl Harbor commenced.

The Little League World Series is played at Howard J. Lamade Stadium. The stadium is actually on Route 15 in South Williamsport, just across the West Branch of the Susquehanna River, in the shadow of Bald Eagle Mountain. South Williamsport is the home of the Little League Headquarters and the World of Little League Museum.

The first time we walked in and saw the stadium is something we would never forget. The perfectly cut grass was a brighter green than I ever remembered seeing. The giant American flag wafting in the breeze beyond the centerfield fence was absolutely majestic. And a place where 10-year-old kids can play in front of 40,000 fans! One word sprung to all of our lips: "Wow!!!!!"

"Are you nervous?" I asked Luke, as we were getting ready to play our opener against the European champion Germany.

"Not really," he answered. "Although I'm kind of nervous about not being nervous. You know what I mean? Everybody keeps acting like I should be nervous, so maybe there's something wrong with me."

I had to smile. "No. There's nothing wrong with you," I said. "I think the guys playing against you should be nervous."

"Thanks. Hey, Mouse. I've been thinking about what Mitch said to you after our last game, thinking maybe that was still bothering you."

"Yeah, maybe a little."

"Well, I was thinking about a way that you can really help us win."

"How's that?"

"You're the smartest guy around, besides Mark, and you know baseball as well as anybody. You should really watch all the other teams play, I mean really watch closely, and see if you can find something that might help us when we play them. You know, like a scout. Look at what pitches guys like to hit. Which of the outfielders have the strongest arms. Stuff like that."

"Okay," I said, and started warming up to the idea. "Yeah. I could do that."

The World Series field that year included four U.S. teams – Washington (that was us), Illinois, New Jersey, and Texas – and four international teams – Germany, Japan, Mexico, and Canada, and the format matched the U.S. teams against the international teams for the first round of games. In the upcoming years teams from the Far East dominated, winning 13 of the next 15 Little League World Series titles, but in 1966 the team to beat was Texas.

The Texas team was a group of giant 12-year-olds from Houston. You talk about needing to see birth certificates. Holy cow, these kids were big and strong. In their games leading up to the series they had scored 10 or more runs in all but one game, and had "mercy ruled" (game ended because of a 10-run lead) their last 3 opponents.

They were led by a couple of identical twins, David and Roger Nelson, who played first base and third base, and seemed to take turns seeing who could hit the ball the hardest and the furthest.

Luke and I met them at the concession stand after we had cruised past Germany, 9-2, and they had blasted Mexico, 10-1. They couldn't have been any nicer.

"Hey, y'all," one of them said (I couldn't tell them apart without their jerseys on). "You boys got a real nice team there. I reckon we might be seein' you in the championship game."

In our opening win over Germany, Luke, batting right-handed, hit the first pitch of the game over the 205-foot leftfield wall for a home run, and in his second at bat, now hitting left-handed, hit the first pitch over the 205-foot right field wall for another home run. After that they decided to walk him. In fact, Luke ended up being walked 6 times in our 3 games in Williamsport, a World Series record.

In the first semifinal game, each of the Nelson twins homered (one was a grand slam) and the big boys from Houston clobbered New Jersey, 11-2.

Our semifinal game was against Japan, who had beaten Illinois in the opening round, 6-3. It was sort of ironic, going up against Germany and then Japan just 21 years after the end of World War II.

It's funny how often in big moments in sports someone unlikely becomes the hero. Just look at the list of Major League baseball World Series MVPs and you'll see a bunch of names of guys who never even made an all-star team but made the biggest splash in the biggest pool at the biggest time. We had one of those high divers ourselves.

Our third baseman was a boy named Gary Radliffe, the second youngest player on the team, and probably the nicest. He was the son of a career military man, and their family had just moved to Bonney Flats that year so he didn't have any long-term friendships on the team. He was quiet, never said a negative word, and called everybody sir.

On the field he was what you would call steady, not flashy. He made all the routine plays, and he got his share of hits, almost always singles. Well, sometime before we got to Williamsport he must have found a magic phone booth to change into his super hero costume, because he emerged as a star.

He had three hits in the opener, and then when the other teams started walking Luke, he came through with clutch hit after clutch hit. Meanwhile, at third base he was diving around and gobbling everything up like "The Human Vacuum Cleaner," the great Brooks Robinson himself.

Gary smashed three doubles, Mike Monroe pitched beautifully, and we beat Japan, 10-2, to advance to the championship game. All that stood between us and being the Little League champions was the small matter of defeating Goliath, also known as Houston.

I had decided to take seriously the scouting assignment that Luke had given me, and figuring that the team to beat was the Texans, I had watched every pitch of their games. But I wasn't sure if anything I had come up with would be useful for us.

"Well, Mouse," Luke asked me before the title game. "Did you see something that might help us?"

"Yeah, I noticed that the Nelson brothers hit the ball a long way, no matter where you pitch them," I said. "I think it would be a good idea to walk them as much as possible."

Luke looked at me as if I had just said "I found out that 2 plus 2 equals 4."

"Wow. Nice going, Mouse," he said sarcastically. "Anything else, Sherlock?"

"Yes, Mr. Smart Aleck," I continued. "Just a couple of little things that might help."

"What?"

"Well, their big starting pitcher, that Gordon Greenfield, he throws almost all fastballs. But when he's getting ready to throw a curveball, it looks like he moves his foot just a few inches to the left on the rubber. If you see him do that, maybe expect him to throw a curve."

Luke nodded and smiled. "Good. That's really good, Mouse."

"And the only other thing," I continued, encouraged, "is their really fast second baseman, Steve Hill. He has kind of a closed stance and chokes up on the bat, except for when he's going to bunt. Then he evens his feet out and drops his hands to the end of the bat. You should look for a bunt if you see him do that."

"Wow. Nice going, Mouse," he said, this time with all sincerity. "That could really help."

It always felt great to make Luke proud.

Chapter 20

<u>Championship Game</u>

"Talent wins games, but teamwork and intelligence wins championships." – Michael Jordan

These days all of the Little League World Series games, as well as many of the regional games, are broadcast on ESPN. But back in those days only the championship game was on TV, shown on Saturday afternoon's Wide World of Sports with Jim McKay. Joining McKay in the booth in 1966 was a man few of us had ever heard of, 37-year-old Keith Jackson, who had just signed on with ABC Sports that year, and would end up announcing, oh, about 8,000 more sporting events over the next 40 years.

Also helping call the action was one of the most courageous men of our lifetime, sports or otherwise, the legendary Jackie Robinson. His autograph is still one of my most prized possessions.

We were the visiting team, and their ace Greenfield came out throwing nothing but fastballs, and they looked like bullets. Luke led off the game with a lineout to centerfield, but then our next four hitters struck out. Gary Radliffe got a single, but he was erased in a double play. So after three innings we had sent the minimum of 9 batters to the plate and hadn't had anybody reach second base.

Meanwhile, William Botts was throwing beautifully for us, pitching very carefully to the Nelson brothers and getting them to chase his wicked curveball in the dirt. Gary and Luke both made diving stops, and we headed to the top of the fourth right where we started, 0-0.

Luke led off the inning for us and chased a fastball way out of the strike zone, then hit the next pitch, another heater, about a mile, but foul. He was down in the count quickly, 0 balls and 2 strikes.

As Greenfield took the catcher's signal for the next pitch, I saw him slide his right foot just a few inches to the left on the rubber. This was it. Curveball coming. Did Luke see it, too?

From our third base dugout I could see Luke's face in the left-handed batter's box. We made eye contact and he gave a tiny, almost imperceptible nod, and I knew he had seen it, too.

Greenfield's curveball started well up and out of the strike zone and broke down to catch the outside corner of the plate. Luke was ready for it, waited on it, and drilled it over the leftfield fence for an opposite field home run and a 1-0 lead.

"You did it, you did it!" I yelled as we all celebrated in the dugout.

"*We* did it," Luke said, hugging me especially tight.

Unfortunately the lead didn't last long. Roger Nelson led off the bottom of the fourth with a walk, and then brother David swung at a pitch almost over his head and tomahawked it out of the park for a home run and a 2-1 Texas lead.

That's how it stood going into the top of the sixth, our final chance. Greenfield seemed tired – his fastball wasn't as blazing, and he no longer trusted his curveball – and we put together a last-inning rally. With one out we got back-to-back doubles from Henry Level and Tom Elya to tie the score, 2-2, and then a groundout to second base sent our runner to third.

This brought Luke to the plate, but they were not about to pitch to him. The Texas manager called for an intentional walk, but their pitcher got too careless and threw one way too high and outside. The ball caromed off the glove of their leaping catcher, and our runner, Tom Elya, raced home for a 3-2 lead.

Now we were just 3 outs away from the championship. But of course it would not come easy. Giants don't go away quietly.

Their leadoff hitter doubled, and then he moved to third on a fly ball to right field. One out and the tying run just 60 feet away. Stepping to the plate was their outstanding second baseman, Steve Hill, and he would be followed by Roger and David Nelson. This spelled trouble with a capital T and that rhymes with D and that stands for Defeat.

Hill watched the first pitch from William curve in for a strike. Then he stepped out of the box, got the sign from his third base coach, and stepped back in.

But as he did so, the position of his feet changed and his hands slid to the nob of the bat. I didn't even have to wonder if Luke saw what I saw. He was already playing way in to cut off the runner at home if a grounder was hit to him, and I saw him creep in a couple of more steps.

Then, just as Botts started his windup, Luke took off running toward home plate. Hill squared to bunt, and just as the ball reached him the runner from third base took off. A squeeze bunt.

Steve Hill placed the bunt perfectly between the pitcher and third base, only it had a slight bit of loft on it. That wouldn't have mattered except that our shortstop, the amazing Luke Daisy, had already run past the pitcher and was closing in fast.

Luke leaped, stretched out, and the ball nestled softly into his glove just before it hit the ground. He slid to his knees, turned and threw to Gary at third to beat their runner who was scrambling back to the bag.

Double play.

Game over.

The Bonney Flats All-Stars, representing the great state of Washington and the Pacific Northwest region, were the 1966 Little League World Series champions.

As the great Keith Jackson would say: Whoa, Nellie!!!!!

We did it. And while it was mostly Luke, William, Gary, Mike, and the others, this time I didn't have any trouble saying "WE."

Chapter 21

Sickness & Grampa Bill

"The Lord is close to the brokenhearted, and saves those who are crushed in spirit." – Psalm 34:18

In September of 1966, a little over a week after our thrilling World Series win, we headed back to Woodlake Elementary for fifth grade. Well, everybody except for me, that is. I had gotten very, very sick.

On the drive home from Williamsport we switched from Beatles songs to Beach Boys songs. We surfed through Pennsylvania (*Surfin' Safari, Surfin' USA, Surfer Girl, Catch A Wave*), raced through Ohio (*Little Deuce Coupe, Shut Down, Fun Fun Fun, I Get Around*), and fell in love through Indiana (*Wouldn't It Be Nice, God Only Knows, Barbara Ann, California Girls*).

By the time we hit Illinois my head started to hurt. I had had headaches before, of course, but this was a throbbing and pounding like I had never experienced. And then my neck got very sore. I figured it was probably from sleeping awkwardly in the station wagon. But when I told my dad that it really hurt my eyes to look at the sun, he knew something was very wrong and drove straight to a hospital.

I wound up in the emergency room of Rush Medical Center in Chicago, where I was diagnosed with bacterial meningitis. I wound up being admitted to the hospital and staying for a week. The Daisys drove our car home, while mom and dad stayed with me until I was released and we flew home.

But when school started the day after Labor Day I was still far too weak to attend. It wouldn't be until the middle of October that I was back at my desk next to Luke and Kenny. During my time at home I had two visitors every day: Mr. Daisy and Luke.

Mr. Daisy came every morning, ate breakfast and prayed with and for me. Luke came every afternoon to bring me my school assignments, tell me Kenny's latest stories, and play games with me. Kenny had continued to play soccer and, without Luke there to score all the goals, had become the star of the team.

A funny thing happened when Luke and I were playing games at that time. I started to win. At least half the time. It didn't take a genius to figure out why.

"I know you're just letting me win because you feel sorry for me," I finally told him.

"What are you talking about, Mouse?" he scoffed. "First of all, I don't feel sorry for you. You get to stay home while the rest of us have to go to school. And second of all, even if I did feel sorry for you I'd never lose to you on purpose. Unless maybe you were dying or something, and not just lying around like a big baby pretending to be sick."

"Okay, Luke. Whatever you say."

Later Mrs. Daisy told me that Luke had been really shook up when they left me in Chicago, and hardly said a word the rest of the drive home.

Bacterial meningitis can be a pretty scary thing if it's not caught soon enough, but it's not too contagious. Still, dad insisted that my visitors wear a surgical mask when they were with me, and avoid any contact.

He probably didn't need to worry about Luke, because I think he had some kind of super human blood type or immunity system. He never got hurt, and he never got sick. He had no allergies. I don't think he ever sunburned. In 12 years he only missed one day of school, and that was for his grandfather's funeral. I always thought there were only two things that could harm Luke: an arrow shot into his Achilles Heel, or kryptonite.

The second time I saw Luke cry was when his grandfather died.

William Board was Mrs. Daisy's dad, and he had raised Sarah and her younger brother Samuel alone after his wife died of polio in 1926 when the kids were 10 and 8. He had grown up in southwest Washington, started working as a lumberjack for the Weyerhaeuser Timber Company in 1912 when he was 16 years old, and eventually worked his way up through the company to be Vice President of the Wood Products Division.

Grampa Bill, as we all called him, was a giant of a man. Big body. Big heart. Big brain. If you liked to play the genetics game, you could find a lot of Daisy trails leading directly to him: Luke's size and strength; Mark's intelligence; Matthew's building/fixing aptitude; and Johnny's sweet nature.

Grampa Bill seemed to love all the kids in the neighborhood and always had treats for us, but he had a special bond with Johnny. He was 60 when Luke and Johnny were born, and he took an early retirement so he could help care for his special youngest grandson. He sold his beautiful 3,000 square-foot home on the lake and built a one bedroom log cabin at the back of the Daisy property so he could be with Johnny every day.

Johnny was almost 4 before he began trying to talk, and besides Mrs. Daisy and Luke, only Grampa Bill could fully understand him. And from that time on, the two of them had a weekly date, every Saturday, to go to the Woodland Park Zoo in Seattle and spend hours together talking, holding hands, and looking at the animals, and then walking around Green Lake. I think just about everybody in that part of Seattle recognized and cared for the unusual pair – the old man and his Down syndrome grandson. After all, Johnny said hi to all of them.

In June of 1968, near the end of our 6th grade year, Grampa Bill died suddenly of a heart attack. He was 72. Luke and I were out playing roof ball, one of our many made-up games, when Mr. Daisy came out and broke the news to us.

"Boys, I have some very sad news to tell you," he said. I could see his eyes were red and he'd been crying. "Grampa Bill died this morning in his sleep. It looks like he had a heart attack and didn't suffer. I'm so sorry."

We just stood there, a couple of stunned 12-year-olds who had never known anyone who had died. I didn't know what to say. After a couple minutes of silence and hugging, Mr. Daisy said, "Luke, I'm going to need you to come in and help your mom and me break the news to Johnny."

That's when Luke started to sob. "Oh Johnny, poor Johnny, what is he going to do? How will he understand this?"

They were all crying when they sat Johnny down to tell him the news, not really knowing if he would have a total meltdown or not really understand what they were telling him. Neither happened.

"Id aw wy," he said. (It's all right.) "Gaba toh me he gway saday, bu he ahway be wi me." (Grampa told me he'd go away someday, but he'd always be with me.)

And he pointed to his heart. "Gaba in hebnow, bu Gaba ahway hee wi me." (Grampa's in heaven now, but Grampa's always here with me.)

The boy with the brain that didn't work quite right seemed to understand things better than any of us.

Chapter 22

Fifth Grade & The Fents

"Little darling, it's been a long cold lonely winter. Little darling, it feels like years since it's been here. Here comes the sun. Here comes the sun. And I say, it's all right." – George Harrison

It wasn't until mid-October of 1966 that I was finally strong enough to return to school, and when I did I was in for quite a shock. Nobody had told me about our fifth grade teacher, Miss Milroy. I'm guessing they were afraid that if they did I would stay home in bed all year long.

We had been spoiled: Mrs. Patty Tanner in first grade, Miss Linda Cleveland in second, Mr. Scott Stokes in third, and Mrs. Katie Rich in fourth grade. Naturally, we thought all teachers were wonderful.

Enter Miss Milroy, although we called her (and I'm not particularly proud of this) Miss Killjoy. It was her first year of teaching, because apparently she hadn't yet figured out that she hated children. Actually, she only disliked the girls. The boys she hated.

As soon as she realized that Luke and Kenny and I were best of friends, she placed us in the far corners of the classroom, as far away from each other as possible. Kenny got in the most trouble with his ability to make people laugh. He drove her crazy with questions like: Why is abbreviation such a long word? How come phonetically isn't spelled with an F? Is there another word for synonym? He spent so much time standing in the corner that he said he should have his mail delivered there.

I made the mistake of correcting her my first week in class (she tried to tell us Minneapolis was the capitol of Minnesota, for crying out loud), so I was often the object of her anger. If I ever develop carpal tunnel syndrome it will be from all the writing I had to do on the chalkboard that school year. (*"I will not act like I am smarter than the teacher."*)

And I thought Luke was going to die when she announced that she would replace the chaos of recess,   with all its running and jumping and playing "like wild savages," with respectable, civilized, square dancing.

Square dancing!!!! Instead of swinging bats we'd be swinging partners. Do-Si-Do instead of dodgeball. Flutter-wheel instead of football. Shoot the Star instead of shooting baskets. California Twirls instead of capture the flag. We would be required to hold hands with girls and put our arms around them. Oh the humanity! We wanted to Allemande left and Allemande right out of school as fast as we could.

"Dad, you gotta help us," I pleaded to my father. "Do something. Talk to her. Talk to Mr. Wood. You gotta get us out of this. This is inhumane. It's probably even illegal."

Luke and Kenny made the same pleas to their parents, but they all fell on deaf ears. In fact we all reported noticeable smirks on our parents' faces regarding our anguish. What kind of monsters didn't even care about their children's suffering?!

"Listen, Michael," dad tried to explain. "Life is not always going to be fun and games. We all have to do a lot of things we don't like to do. And everybody isn't always going to see things the same way you do.

"Now Miss Killjoy, err, I mean Miss Milroy, is your teacher, and you need to do what she asks, and do it without grumbling or whining," he continued. "Do you understand?"

"I guess so," I said reluctantly. "But I sure miss my meningitis."

Between square dancing and Miss Killjoy's Gestapo-like ways, fifth grade was looking like a very, very long and difficult school year. But a couple of things happened during Christmas break that changed everything.

The first was that Miss Milroy resigned. When we came back to school in early January we had a different teacher, Mrs. Ellen Hunter. Mrs. Hunter actually seemed to like kids, and best of all, she reinstated recess and put the kibosh on square dancing. "Boys and girls need to run and play," she said, stating what I had assumed was obvious to everyone. Mrs. Hunter instantly became my favorite person in the whole wide world.

We never heard what happened to Miss Milroy, whether she left on her own or Mr. Wood asked her to leave because of parental pressure. But we liked to guess what became of her.

"Professional square dance caller," I guessed.

"I'm saying a house fell on her," Kenny added.

"I know," Luke surmised. "CIA torture specialist."

"Forsooth," Kenny agreed. (That's Shakespearean for "indeed.") "Or else she's gone off to start The Fourth Reich."

The second thing that happened during that Christmas break was every bit as wonderful. The Fent family moved to the Brightwood Park Apartments just outside our neighborhood, which meant that Ellie would be joining us in our Woodlake Elementary fifth grade class.

It didn't take long to realize that not only was Ellie super fast, but she was also super fun. She loved sports, and was good at all of them. Although she was the prettiest girl in the class, she didn't act like a girly girl. She didn't even giggle. I had the feeling she would have hated square dancing as much as we did. It was almost like she was a boy, only she looked and smelled better. Right away she was hanging out with us at recess and after school.

The Three Musketeers had become the Fantastic Four.

The Fent family was much different than the rest of ours. We spent very little time at their apartment, usually just for Ellie to change clothes, but we were there enough to know that her parents were — and I'm pretty sure this is not the correct psychiatric term — real weirdos. Mr. Fent didn't work, as far as we could tell, rarely left the house, and always had a cigarette in his hand. He would usually offer us a beer (we were in elementary school, for crying out loud), and ask us strange questions, like how much money did our parents make, or did we really believe that JFK had been assassinated.

Mrs. Fent was always barefoot, wore miniskirts, flowers in her hair, and insisted on hugging us, which made us feel very uncomfortable. She was the only parent we knew who wanted us to call her by her first name, which she said was Rainbow. Ellie called her Betsy, which was her real first name until she decided to go by Rainbow sometime in the mid-60s. Mrs. Fent did not like being called Betsy. That was one of the few things she did not think was "groovy."

Ellie's brothers, Larry and Tony, were 5 and 6 years older than she, so when the family moved close to us both boys had already been in and kicked out of high school. One or the other was usually hanging around their place, and Ellie warned us not to look directly into their eyes because they would see it as some sort of a challenge. It was kind of like living with a couple of wild dogs.

Once, when we were in ninth grade, Ellie said something the older brother Tony didn't like and he shoved her hard enough to knock her over. Luke walked slowly across the room, and Tony, then 21, sneered at Ellie's 15-year-old friend with a look that said "what are you gonna do about it?" Luke punched him in the nose so hard that I think you could have heard the sound two houses down. Tony crumpled like a house of cards.

Luke bent down and said quietly in his ear, "You'll be very sorry if you ever touch your sister again."

Tony just lied there bleeding and moaning. Of course I had to put in my two cents as we walked out.

"I'm pretty sure he's not kidding," I said.

Hoppy then added, "You should probably get that nose checked."

Tony's elevator may not have gone all the way to the top floor, but he did get his nose checked (broken), he knew that Luke wasn't kidding, and he never touched his little sister again.

By the time the family had moved into their apartment Mr. & Mrs. Fent had decided that being parents just wasn't their cup of tea, so they pretty much abdicated all of their mom and dad responsibilities. In August of 1969, with both Larry and Tony in jail for robbing one of the neighbor's apartments, Mr. & Mrs. Fent hitchhiked across the country to be among the 400,000 who gathered on Max Yasgur's 600-acre dairy farm for the three day love-drug-mud-music fest known as Woodstock. They were considerate enough to leave a nice note and plenty of milk, bread, peanut butter, and macaroni & cheese for Ellie. She was 13.

It really was one of the most remarkable things that Ellie – kind, considerate, loyal, loving – emerged from that environment. In classic Ken Carew funny-but-true fashion, Hoppy said that she was "our very own, real life, Marilyn Munster." (Marilyn was the beautiful young woman who lived with a Frankenstein, a bride of Frankenstein, a vampire, and a wolf boy in the 60s sitcom *The Munsters*.)

Ellie could almost match wits with Kenny – almost – and had a way of making even Luke not take himself too seriously. In some ways she was the most grown-up of the four of us, but in other ways she seemed the most childish. She still slept with her beloved Winnie the Pooh blanket, and she called all of us Bear: Kenny Bear, Lukey Bear, and Mikey Bear. Basically, she made our nearly perfect little world even better.

In the long run, fifth grade turned out to be not so bad after all.

Chapter 23

<u>Sixth Grade</u>

"Be at your best when your best is needed." – John Wooden, Pyramid of Success

Trying to rank all of Luke's amazing athletic accomplishments from top to bottom would be a very challenging task, but you could make a very good case for placing what he did during our sixth grade year, from the fall of '67 to the spring of '68, right at the top.

Every fall, starting in 1961, the National Football League and the Ford Motor Company combined to sponsor a nationwide Punt, Pass, & Kick competition for kids age 6 through 15. Each contestant would get one punt, one pass, and one placekick, and their score would be the combined yardage of the three, minus the yards that each attempt went astray from a centerline. Whoever had the highest total in their age group would advance, first through the district, then the state, past the regional, and finally to the national championships.

Luke had continued to get bigger and stronger, so that as an 11-year-old he was 5-foot-5, 110 pounds, the size of the average 14-year-old. (His birth certificate was never far from Mrs. Daisy's purse.) It came as no surprise to anyone when he won the first three competitions, although he was the only 11-year-old nationwide who had the top yardage in all three areas (punting, passing, and kicking) for all three competitions.

The national finals were held on Saturday, December 9 at the Los Angeles Coliseum during the pre-game of the Green Bay vs. Los Angeles NFL game. Many of the 76,000-plus in attendance that day had shown up early, eager to watch their Coastal Division champion Rams, coached by the legendary George Allen, take on the defending Super Bowl champion Packers, coached by their even more legendary coach Vince Lombardi.

Several of the Cateere, Daisy, and Carew families were among that legion of fans, far more interested in the pre-game than the real game. Our folks had taken us out of school a few days early (with the blessing of our sixth grade teacher, Mr. Cameron Packard), so we caravanned down in three cars, and dad used some connections to get us 12 tickets to the game (in addition to the four that Ford and the NFL provided for the Daisys).

There was no statistical information to know how well the other 7 boys in his age group had done during their earlier competitions, so we had no idea what Luke's chances were of winning. Except that we really did. It was Luke Daisy, after all.

His punt travelled 52 yards and hit right on the centerline. His kick also went exactly 52 yards and also landed on the centerline. It was the farthest he had ever punted or placekicked, and he was the leader in both events.

He pretty much had the title wrapped up, but he wanted to win the passing portion for another clean sweep. The crowd let out a gasp when he heaved it 56 yards, but it was four yards off center for another 52-yard total. That was the second best throw, as another boy tossed it 53 yards and right on the centerline. I could never remember if his name was Joe Pennsylvania from Montana or Joe Montana from Pennsylvania, although by the early '80s it became pretty clear to me which was correct.

So Luke's total of 52 + 52 + 52 = 156 yards won easily, and is still the national record for 11-year-olds. (Also, the Rams beat the Packers, 27-24, so it was pretty much a perfect day.)

Luke Daisy, you've just become the national PP&K champion, what are you going to do now?

We all went to Disneyland the next day for an early Christmas present (thanks again to Ford and the NFL buying us 16 tickets) and to celebrate our very own national champion. Luke was a little disappointed in himself for his pass being off line, but the Jungle Cruise, Matterhorn, and the rest of the *Happiest Place on Earth* managed to cheer him up just fine.

And that was just the beginning of his sixth grade magic. In the winter the Spalding Corporation sponsored a national Hoop Shoot competition for fifth- and sixth-graders. Each boy would shoot 25 free throws, and whoever made the most would advance. The set-up was the same, with district, state, and regional competitions leading to the national finals.

Luke won the district, making 21 of 25.

He won the state, hitting 22 of 25.

And he won the regional, sinking 23 of 25.

In the two weeks leading up to the nationals, Mr. Packard stayed after school and kept the gym open, and also opened it on Saturdays, so Luke could practice. Kenny, Ellie, and I took turns rebounding and passing it back to Luke while he shot about 200 free throws a day. "Twenty-three is not going to be good enough," he said.

The finals were held in the Houston Astrodome on January 20, 1968, at halftime of *The Game of The Century*, when Elvin Hayes and the Houston Cougars beat Johnny Wooden's UCLA Bruins, 71-69. It was one of only two losses for UCLA during Lew Alcindor's 90 games there. Almost 53,000 fans were there to witness the action, in addition to the millions who were watching on television.

What the TV viewers did not get to watch was the halftime Hoop Shoot finals, which was just about as exciting.

Luke was the seventh of eight to shoot, and the number to beat was 22. His first shot looked good, but hit the back rim and bounced out. He took the ball, looked down, shook his head, and took a deep breath.

And then made his next 24 shots.

Only one boy left who could top him, a wild-haired country boy who had just turned 11 in December from the tiny town of French Lick, Indiana.

And wouldn't you know? That kid, who was even taller than Luke, made all 25 shots, almost all of them swishes, to win the title. Luke would have to "settle" for being the second best shooter in his age group in the whole country.

In January of 1964 a University of Oregon track athlete, Phil Knight, and his coach, Bill Bowerman, founded a new sporting goods company called *Blue Ribbon Sports*. Seven years later a Portland State University graphics design student named Carolyn Davidson came up with a simple swoosh for a logo, and Blue Ribbon Sports became a little business known as Nike, Inc. With close to 50,000 employees and worth around $30 billion,

Nike is the largest supplier of athletic shoes and apparel in the world.

But in the spring of 1968, Blue Ribbon Sports was still trying to make a name for itself and expand throughout the country. With baseball as our national pastime and the nation's most popular sport, they decided to focus on youth baseball as their most fertile market for growth.

And so they sponsored a nationwide competition for 12-year-old boys in various baseball skills: throwing for distance, throwing for accuracy, hitting for distance, and timed running around the bases. Spokesman for the event was recently retired New York Yankee second baseman, Bobby Richardson. Not only was Richardson one of the greatest World Series performers ever ('60 MVP, '62 defensive hero, '64 record for most hits), but he was one of the finest gentlemen to ever play professional sports. And he just happened to be one of Luke's all-time sports heroes.

All of the competitors got a Blue Ribbon Sports t-shirt and a Blue Ribbon Sports baseball cap, and those that made it to the finals got a Bobby Richardson-autographed baseball. Luke added that to his collection from the year which included Bart Starr, Roman Gabriel, Vince Lombardi, George Allen, Elvin Hayes, Lew Alcindor, and Johnny Wooden. Not too shabby for a sixth grade kid.

Oh yeah, about the competition. Let me start by telling you about two of the boys that did not win. One was from St. Paul (the real capitol of Minnesota), representing the Midwest Region, a kid by the name of Paul Molitor. You can find his name in Cooperstown as a Hall of Famer. And the other was a boy from Youngstown, Ohio, representing the Great Lakes Region, named Dave Dravecky. The lefty went on to be a star pitcher for the San Diego Padres and San Francisco Giants, but more importantly a great man of courage and character who inspired thousands with his battle against cancer that eventually resulted in the amputation of his pitching arm.

Those two finished second and third. First place, of course, went to a boy from Bonney Flats, Washington named Luke Daisy, whose legend just kept growing and growing.

Chapter 24

1968, Special Olympics

"Let me win. But if I cannot win, let me be brave in the attempt."
– Special Olympics Motto

While Luke's athletic achievements would be hard to rank, his greatest athletic joy would be easy to pick. It came in the summer of '68, and it didn't even involve him.

The year 1968 was one of the most impactful in the history of our great country. In April a monster shot and killed one of our nation's great heroes, Dr. Martin Luther King, Jr. Two months later a crazy man shot and killed presidential candidate Senator Robert Kennedy, the younger brother of our previously slain president. The Vietnam War was at its peak, as were the nationwide protests of it. There was rioting in over 100 cities. A sitting president decided not to run for re-election, and the Democratic National Convention wound up in chaos with 10,000 demonstrators clashing with 23,000 police and national guardsman, resulting in almost 700 arrests.

A lot of that reached down into our 12-year-old kid world, and we became more and more aware that the world could be a scary and far-from-perfect place.

Even the sports world was crazy. In January hockey player Bill Masterson died from a head injury, the only player ever to die as a result of an injury suffered in an NHL game. In April the start of the Major League Baseball season was postponed because of the assassination of Dr. King. A week later the actual winner of the Masters golf tournament (Roberto DiVicenzo) was disqualified for signing an incorrect scorecard (making Bob

Goalby the winner). The same month a new heavyweight boxing champion was crowned (Jimmy Ellis) because the real champion, Muhammad Ali, had been stripped of his title for refusing his military service after being drafted. In May the winner of the Kentucky Derby (Dancer's Image) was disqualified when traces of a banned substance were discovered in his system (giving the victory to Forward Pass). In October two of our Olympic track stars (Tommie Smith and John Carlos) were stripped of their medals for protesting during the Mexico City Games. And in November NBC cut away from what turned out to be a thrilling NFL finish between the Jets and Raiders to show the movie *Heidi*. (Twenty years later *The Heidi Game* was voted the most memorable NFL regular season game in history.)

But the sports world also provided us with some great and positive memories from that year. Vince Lombardi led Green Bay to its second straight Super Bowl victory in his last game as Packers' coach. Beloved Arthur Ashe became the only African American man to ever win the U.S. Open singles title in tennis. Denny McLain won a phenomenal 31 games for the Detroit Tigers. And the great Bob Gibson had a record-setting year for the St. Louis Cardinals, including an amazing 17 strikeouts in a World Series game.

Another true highlight in 1968 kid world was the introduction of the Big Mac. *Two all-beef patties, special sauce, lettuce, cheese, pickles, onions – on a sesame seed bun.* We all knew the jingle by heart. And once or twice a month, after church on Sunday, we'd drive to Tacoma, plunk down our 45 cents on the McDonald's counter, and feast on the new taste treat. Sometimes we'd add fries and a Coke, and still get change back from a dollar. Life was pretty good.

For the Daisy and Cateere families, however, all of that took a back seat to what happened in Chicago on July 20 of that year.

In the summer of 1962, President Kennedy's younger sister, Eunice Kennedy Shriver, began a day camp at her home in Potomac, Maryland, to promote sports and other physical activities for children with intellectual disabilities. Camp Shriver was an effort to honor her sister, Rosemary, who had been born intellectually challenged.

Camp Shriver was an annual event which continued to grow, leading to the vision of a nationwide, and eventually worldwide, sporting event for the disabled. Thus was born the Special Olympics, which debuted at Soldier Field in Chicago on July 20, 1968.

An advisory committee, chaired by Mrs. Shriver, was set up to organize and prepare for the event. Members of that committee included 1960 Olympic decathlon champion Rafer Johnson, several other dignitaries, and one Dr. Robert Cateere of Bonney Flats, Washington – my dad. Apparently dad and Mrs. Shriver's husband, Sargent Shriver, had become friends while serving together briefly in the Navy near the end of World War II.

Nearly 1,000 athletes from the United States and Canada participated in those first games, including 12-year-old Johnny Daisy. The competitions were limited to swimming, field hockey, and track & field. Johnny could barely swim or handle a hockey stick, and he certainly wasn't very fast. But he was strong, and he could throw a ball a long ways, often trying to emulate his twin brother. He qualified to compete in Chicago in the softball throw.

Each contestant was allowed to have a coach on the field with them – Johnny chose Luke, of course – and each athlete was given 3 throws. Johnny's first throw was very short, which we attributed to nerves, and when his second throw was even shorter, Luke could tell something wasn't right.

"What's the matter, Johnny?" he asked. "You can throw it way farther than that."

"Ayscare, Wookie," he answered (I'm scared, Luke.) "Too mee peepah." (Too many people.)

Johnny did not like crowds, and he did not like loud noises.

"Do you remember the oath they had you say, Johnny?" Luke encouraged. "Let's say it together."

"Let me win. But if I cannot win, let me be brave in the attempt," they recited together.

"Do you know what it means to be brave?" Luke asked.

"It means not to be scared," Johnny answered.

"No. It means to do what you have to do even though you're scared. It means to not let being scared get the best of you. Do you understand?"

"Yeah, but you never scared, Wookie."

"We all get scared sometimes, Johnny. I get scared plenty of times."

"What you do?"

"Well, sometimes I think of those verses mom and dad taught us from Joshua. Remember? Let's say them together."

"Be strong and courageous. Do not be terrified, do not be discouraged. For the Lord your God will be with you wherever you go."

"Does that help?" Luke asked.

"Yeah, but there's still lots of people," Johnny said.

"Well, don't look at them. Just look at me. I'll be at the end of the field. Just pretend that you're throwing the ball to me. Remember: you don't have to be brave for a long time. Just for a minute. You can do it."

"Okay. I'll try."

When Johnny lined up for his third and final throw, he was in last place in the competition of his age group. Luke stood at the far end of the field waving his arms for Johnny to look only at him.

But Johnny looked up in the stands for a long time, and then up to the sky. And then he smiled his crooked smile, took a few clumsy strides, and uncorked a mighty throw, maybe the farthest he had ever thrown a ball. It sailed well past the final marker, and our very own Johnny Daisy was the first-ever 12-year-old Special Olympics Softball Throw Gold Medalist. (Johnny wore that gold medal every day for the rest of his life.)

Luke raced to embrace his twin brother and our little cheering section went wild, screams of joy and hugs and tears all around.

After the medal ceremony Mr. Daisy asked Johnny, "How come you were able to throw it so much farther on your last throw, son?"

"Wookie hep me bebay," he explained. (Luke helped me be brave.) "And I 'membered the verse. And I saw all of you, but no Grampa Bill. But I 'membered what he said."

And again he pointed to his heart. "He said he would always be here. And he was."

I don't think any of us had any doubt about it.

Chapter 25

<u>Lincoln Lake</u>

"We had joy, we had fun, we had seasons in the sun." – Terry Jacks

Our grade school days at Woodlake Elementary were over, and in September of 1968 we would start seventh grade at Lewis & Clark Junior High School. So that meant August was our last big hurrah before we had to face school *without any recess*. What a terrifying thought!

Fortunately, August of '68 was the hottest and driest month on record for Bonney Flats, so the five of us – Luke, Johnny, Kenny, Ellie, and I - spent almost every day at Lincoln Lake.

Lincoln Lake was our local treasure, a beautiful 6-acre body of water that sat smack dab in the middle of Bonney Flats and served as the boundary for all of the secondary schools. Whether you lived on the north, east, south, or west side determined which of the four junior highs you would attend, and everyone who lived on the west side – that was us – went to Paul Revere High School, while those on the east side went to Madison.

Lincoln Lake had it all: swimming, water skiing, inner tubing, and fishing (stocked rainbow trout and kokanee, yellow perch, rock bass, coastal cutthroat, and brown bullhead catfish). The rumor was that it was so deep that nobody had ever been able to measure its depth in the center of the lake, and there were probably bodies dumped there of people who had run afoul of local gangsters or mafia types. We didn't actually know of any local gangsters or mafia types, but whenever we heard that somebody was no longer around (they had most likely moved), invariably somebody would offer the theory: "Lincoln Lake got another one."

On the east side of the lake was McLaren Park, with most of the city's baseball and soccer fields, where a lot of Luke's legendary moments took place. (In fact, years later it was renamed Luke Daisy Park.) There were also tennis courts, basketball courts, bike trails, and lots of picnic tables.

But the main attraction was on our west side of the lake, Johnson Park, named for the first mayor of Bonney Flats, Cooper Johnson. There was actually an admission charge to Johnson Park – one dollar – because the swimming area featured a 25-foot high slide, a trapeze with an 8-foot drop into the water, and diving platforms of 10-, 20-, 30-, and 40-feet.

There was a lifeguard on duty, but you didn't have to sign a liability waiver or bring a parental consent form. It was a much different time – there was a lot of "at your own risk" kind of thinking, which everyone understood. And if someone did something stupid and got hurt, the reaction wasn't: "Somebody's going to get sued." It was: "Why'd he do something dumb like that?" The main nod to safety was that you had to be at least 12 years old to use any of the water features, so that summer was our first time experiencing the thrills, and fears, of Johnson Park. (Of course, years later the diving platforms were removed when some dumb kid did something stupid and his parents sued the city and some dumb jury awarded them millions of dollars.)

We'd get up and do our chores, pack a lunch (usually a baloney sandwich, chips, an apple, and a quarter for a soda from the concession stand), hop on our bikes and ride the three miles to the lake. We'd usually arrive by 11 am and stay until the park closed at 6 p.m. Each of us had planned for this and saved up enough of our allowance money so that we could enjoy the whole month of August without having to worry about how we would manage it financially.

Johnny would always bring a couple loaves of stale bread because he loved to feed the ducks. One of dad's favorite patients, Fred Boback, managed the local Piggly Wiggly grocery store and would save the old loaves for Johnny instead of throwing them out. When the bread was gone, Johnny was happy to play in the sand and the shallow water. The rest of us headed straight for the diving platforms.

I'll never forget the first time. We decided we'd start on the lowest platform, the 10-footer. Luke was first, of course, and he actually did a flip off of it, no hesitation. Ellie also jumped off without giving it a second thought. I was next and, yes, I did pause at the edge — hey, it looked a lot farther from up there than it did from the dock — but I managed to jump without screaming.

Then it was Kenny's turn, and when he stepped to the edge it was far more than hesitation, it was outright fear. He held onto the railing with a death grip, both hands, and peaked out over the platform to the water which must have seemed a mile down for him. I thought he might pass out. We waited for several minutes, calling out encouragement to him.

"You can do it, Kenny Bear," Ellie shouted.

"All it takes is one little step," I added. "It doesn't hurt a bit."

"Come on pal," Ellie said. "You'll be so glad you did it."

Finally Luke chimed in.

"Hoppy, if you don't want to do it, you don't have to," he yelled. "It's okay, buddy. Nobody will think any less of you. Just come back down the ladder if you really don't want to jump.

Kenny nodded, his shoulders relaxed, and you could see the relief on his face. But as he turned to walk back down the ladder, Luke started making chicken noises.

"Bawk, bawk, bawk, bawk," he hollered up at our friend.

Kenny turned and glared at Luke, and then ran and leaped off the platform, screaming all the way down.

I just looked at Luke, shaking my head.

"Hey," he said. "Sometimes shame can be a great motivator."

Kenny swam to the dock with a big smile on his face. "Don't even try to get me to go off the 20-footer," he said. "No way am I even going up there."

"Okay," Luke agreed. "But aren't you glad you jumped off that one?"

"All I can say," Kenny replied, "is that I'm very, very glad I'm wearing a brown swimsuit."

Then we headed up to the 20-footer, and again Luke didn't think twice. Off he went in a swan dive, which he later admitted hurt his head a little. Ellie paused for just a second, but then jumped straight in.

Now it was my turn for the big hesitation. I managed to block out the shouts from below, as well as the people waiting in line behind me telling me to hurry up and make up my mind. All that was left were the two debating voices in my head.

Voice 1: "You can do it, Michael."

Voice 2: "Don't do it, Michael."

Voice 1: "Come on. What's the worst that could happen?"

Voice 2: "You could die."

Voice 1: "You're not gonna die, stupid."

Voice 2: "Probably not. But it might really hurt."

Voice 1: "Just do it. Ellie did it. You can do it, too."

And so Voice 1 won the debate and I jumped, but Voice 2 had the last word. All the way down he shouted in my head: "You fooooooooooooooool."

I didn't die. I remembered to point my toes and enter the water as vertically as possible. Good for me. Unfortunately, I forgot to close my eyes, hold my breath, or put my arms down at my side. Bad for me. Hitting the water after a 20-foot jump with your arms out to your side is not a good idea. Owwwwwww!!!!! Swallowing a gallon of lake water: also not recommended. But survival is a good thing, and I did manage to smile as I reached my group on the dock.

"Well done, Mouse," Luke praised. "Now, are you ready for the 30-footer?"

"Hmmmm, let me give that one some thought," I said, tapping my temple with my index finger. "You know, I think maybe I'll just pass."

"Yeah, I think I will too," Ellie said. I was pretty sure that she wanted to go up but maybe didn't want me to feel bad.

"No, you should do it, Ellie," I said. "Go on. I think you'll be glad you did."

She nodded and smiled. "Okay, Mikey Bear. Let's go Luke."

So the two of them headed up to the 30-footer. I watched my two incredibly athletic friends walking away together, and even though I loved them both, and Ellie was kind of like one of the guys, there was a small part of me that felt a little bit ... what? Jealous? Sad? Left out? It wasn't hard to see that the two of them belonged together, but I couldn't deny that my heart still fluttered whenever I saw her. Oh well.

Up they went, and they actually jumped off the 30-footer together, waving to Kenny and me on the way down with goofy looks on their faces. That was high enough for Ellie, but Luke had to go jump off the 40-footer before we could get on with our day. Although Luke had told Johnny that he got scared plenty of times, I think it may have been one of the only times he lied to his brother. I really think he was fearless. Of course, it's not hard to be that way when you're indestructible.

On one of our Lincoln Lake days we encountered the bully Bruce Junkers and a couple of his evil minions, Marv Snortberry and Mitch Templeton, who were about to enter ninth grade. Johnny, Ellie, Kenny, and I were sitting in the grass, playing a game of Crazy Eights. Luke had gone to the concession stand.

"Well, well, well, if it isn't the retards," Bruce snorted. Marv and Mitch sneered along. "Who let you punks in?"

"What do you want, Bruce?" I asked. "Are you just here to cause trouble?"

"Yeah," Kenny added. "Why don't you fellows move along. You're blocking the sun."

"Looks like you've been in the sun too long already, boy," Bruce spat out, with his cohorts chuckling along.

Kenny burst out laughing, slapping his legs in an exaggerated fashion.

"That's a good one, man," he said. "Because I'm Black. Ha ha. Did you just make that up? I'm sure nobody has ever said that before."

Bruce just stared at him, looking ready to kill.

"But I have to wonder," Kenny continued, now acting serious. "What's with all the vitriolic vituperations? Why the deprecation and disparagement? What is the reason for your asperity and gaffigations?"

Bruce now looked confused, like Kenny was some kind of an alien.

"And furthermore," Kenny went on. "If you prick us, do we not bleed? If you tickle us, do we not laugh? If you poison us, do we not die?

"And if you wrong us," he emphasized. "shall we not seek revenge?"

Then he turned to us and explained, "*The Merchant of Venice*, Act III, Scene I."

That's when Luke returned from the concession stand. He set his pop down and stood facing Bruce, who backed up a step. Marv and Mitch backed up two steps.

Bruce was big for a ninth grader. Luke was just about as big. Bruce was strong for a ninth grader. Luke was stronger.

"Well if it isn't Puke Pansy," Bruce said, trying, but failing, not to sound nervous. He had not bargained for this, and you could almost see his tiny brain cells trying to figure out a way out of it without losing too much face in front of his toadies.

Part of me wanted to see Bruce pay for his obnoxious ways, but I did not want to see Luke beat him up and then get in trouble, and probably result in us being asked to leave the park.

Johnny stood up and touched Luke's arm. "Dohna hurhim, Wookie," he said once again. (Don't hurt him, Lukie.)

The two stood there staring at each other for a few seconds while we all wondered what would happen next. Well, we all wondered except for Ellie, because she knew what would happen next.

There are several places that a boy does not want to be kicked, but I think most every boy would agree on where is the worst place to be kicked. Standing right behind Bruce, Ellie delivered a fierce, full-speed kick to that exact spot, and the bully dropped to his knees with a very high-pitched whine and two hands instinctively but belatedly guarding his damaged valuables.

Wide-eyed and open-mouthed, Marv and Mitch abandoned their wounded leader without a second thought. Nice friends, huh? Meanwhile we all turned our gaze from the suffering sack of sewage on the ground to our friend Ellie, who looked like it had been just another day at the office.

"Who is this dirtbag, anyway?" she asked.

I just shook my head in wonder at my group of friends, but I had to ask Kenny.

"Gaffigations?"

He smiled and shrugged. "Yeah, I made that one up."

Chapter 26

Electric Football, Sonics, & Seventh Grade

"Life is playfulness. We need to play so that we can rediscover the magic all around us." – Flora Colao

At that time in Bonney Flats, elementary school was first through sixth grades, junior high was seventh through ninth grades, and high school was 10th through 12th grades. So in the fall of '68 we were leaving behind the comfort and power of being grade school royalty, for the uncertainty and unimportance of being junior high rabble. We had heard horror stories about how the big bad ninth graders would stuff helpless and hapless seventh graders into garbage cans, or worse yet, duct tape them to hallway pillars. We knew nobody would mess with Luke, but he wouldn't always be there to protect us.

And we would have to go to classes without our best friends always by our side, which felt altogether wrong. I had three classes with Ellie and two each with Luke and Kenny, and we all had the same lunch break, so it could have been a lot worse. And that first day fear – okay, for me it was more like terror – quickly evaporated when we realized it was not a prison or concentration camp, but just school. Different format, some different kids, lots of different teachers, *no recess*, but in the end, just school.

Lewis & Clark Junior High was the newest of the district's four junior highs – 2 years old – so everything was still in good shape. The walls were clean and the roof didn't leak. The desks were still pretty shiny.

And perhaps best of all, we didn't seem to have any of those big bad ninth graders we had feared. They either ignored us or were nice to us, which was about all we could hope for. (Bruce Junkers and his knucklehead pals went to Harrison Junior High on the south side of the lake.)

Our school's teams were named the Pathfinders, which was very unusual and I thought really cool. Unless you were a cheerleader.

Give me a **P**

Give me an **A**

Give me a **T**

Give me an **H**

Give me an **F**

Give me an **I**

Give me an **N**

Give me a **D**

(Pause for breath. Now where were we? Oh yeah ...)

Give me an **E**

Give me an **R**

Give me an **S**

What's that spell?

Ummmm, let me think .... Oh yeah. *Pathfinders.*

One of the positive things about junior high was that, instead of one great teacher, we had several. There was Mr. Tony Lucarelli, our Italian-American English teacher who was always smiling and singing. "I'll tell you what, Mikey," he would say when asked how he was doing. "Anytime you wake up on the top side of the dirt, it's a good day, am I right?"

And there was Mr. Ralph Jenks, our drawlin', Arkansas-born P.E. teacher who had an unusual way of expressing his enjoyment. "I haven't had this much fun," he would say, "since the hogs ate my baby brother."

And there was the wonderful Miss Melinda Rice, our typing teacher. I think all the boys had a crush on her. "Do you think it would help or hurt my grade," Kenny asked us, "if I were to type out *'You are beautiful, Miss Rice. I'll be 21 in about eight years. Will you wait for me?'* "

"No, I don't think that's a good idea, Hoppy," Luke answered.

"Even if I typed it perfectly. And added *'I love you'*," he pleaded.

"Still no," I affirmed.

The problem for us that year was that there was no interscholastic football or basketball for seventh graders. The ninth graders played Varsity and the eighth graders played Junior Varsity, but we lowly seventh graders had to settle for intramural flag football in the fall and intramural basketball in the winter.

So we played against our classmates in flag football (Luke dominated) and in basketball (Luke dominated even more).

The good news was that, as hot and dry as our summer had been, our fall was every bit as wet and cold. So it turned out to be a pretty good season to be spending our time mostly indoors. And instead of real football, we settled for playing an entire NFL season of Electric Football.

In the late 1940s the Tudor Metal Products Company in New York City invented electric football. Played on a 24-inch by 13-inch metal vibrating field, the two competitors would line up, in formation, their 11 plastic players attached to a weighted metal base, activate the game switch, and watch how far the ball carrier could get before he was tackled (touched) by one of the defenders.

We took it very, very seriously.

All four of us – Luke, Ellie, Kenny, and I – had gotten a game for our birthdays or Christmas. We each had the 1967 flagship model 620 with the improved metal surface, cardboard fan backdrop and scoreboard, and NFL style goalposts. And we used allowance money to buy several sets of extra players. A couple of Kenny's artistic sisters – Hope and Joy – agreed to paint our players in the uniform colors of NFL teams.

Each of us had 3 different NFL teams, so every team played a 9-game schedule. Statistics, scores and standings were kept in the Official B.F.E.F.L. (Bonney Flats Electric Football League) Notebook.

Although each team had a TTQ (triple threat quarterback who could run, pass, or kick), completing a pass in electric football was extremely difficult. You'd have to turn the activation switch off, place the small oval magnetized ball on your TTQ's arm, bend him backwards and release him in hopes the ball would find one of your receivers downfield. I believe we wound up with more lost balls than completed passes. Electric football was so much a running game that even Woody Hayes would have approved.

For our games in Green Bay we would pour a little laundry detergent on the field to simulate the frozen tundra of Lambeau Field. Once, when Kenny's power cord got too frayed and wouldn't work, we tried to play by placing the field on the dryer and turning it on. But the vibrations were too powerful, the players bounced off the field completely, and we had to reschedule the game at my house.

Each of the players had thin plastic prongs or brushes, also known as their "cleats", attached to the bottom of their bases. Before each play you could adjust their "cleats" by brushing them in a certain direction to influence which way they would move along the board. Midway through the season Ellie got suspended for two games because she was caught using pliers to lengthen her players' cleats and make them move faster. She tried to claim ignorance, that she didn't know it was against the rules, but the vote was 3-1 against her. She called us "wimpy crybabies," but other than that took it pretty well.

Heading into the championship game I felt good about the chances of my Browns against Luke's Rams. My star running back was Leroy Kelly, and I could adjust his "cleats" so that he would move straight and then angle slightly to the left so that when he hit the edge of the field he would turn straight upfield toward the end zone. My little plastic Leroy Kelly, much like the real one, scored a lot of touchdowns.

But shortly before the game started, a sad realization hit me: this was Luke I was up against. Luke never lost. And sure enough, it turns out Luke had stayed up all night figuring out how to do the nearly impossible: complete passes and kick field goals with that tiny magnet ball. His little Roman Gabriel threw to his small Jack Snow and his diminutive Bernie Casey for several touchdowns, his miniature Bruce Gossett kicked two field goals, and the Luke Daisy Rams defeated the Mouse Cateere Browns, 34-12, to capture the coveted B.F.E.F.L. championship.

The other activity that occupied so much of our time in the fall and winter of '68-69 was our beloved Seattle Sonics. It was kind of tough to be a Seattle-area kid who loved sports in the early '60s because we had no big league teams in football, basketball, baseball, or hockey. We wanted one in the worst way. And in the fall of 1967 we got one in the worst way.

When the NBA decided to expand from 10 to 12 teams, Los Angeles businessman Sam Schulman was chosen to head up a franchise to be located in Seattle. Boeing had just been awarded a contract for the SST Project, and so it was only natural that our new team be called the Supersonics.

We were very bad - 23 wins and 59 losses – but we didn't even mind. We had our own team! In fact, the Sonics finished sixth in the league in attendance, and we took great pride in the fact that we didn't finish in last place. That dishonor went to the other expansion team, the San Diego Rockets. Those poor schlocks only won 15 games.

We went to as many games as we could – our cheap seat tickets were only $4 - either riding the bus downtown or bumming a ride from one of Kenny's sisters. We even had our own superstar: Walt Hazzard. The former UCLA guard averaged 24 points a game, made the NBA All-Star team, and made losing a lot more palatable for us kids.

And so we were sad (crushed, devastated) when the Sonics traded our man Hazzard after that first season to the St. Louis Hawks for somebody named Lenny Wilkens. We had heard that Wilkens was pretty good, but he was no Walt Hazzard.

There are times in each of our lives when we are wrong. But there are few times, hopefully, when you are as colossally, undeniably, unbelievably wrong as we were. Lenny Wilkens was awesome!!!! He was a 13-time NBA All-Star, led the league in assists one year, was an All-Star game MVP, named as one of the NBA's 50 greatest players of all time, inducted into the basketball Hall of Fame three times (as a player, a coach, and part of the 1992 Olympic Dream Team), and perhaps best of all, coached our Sonics to their only NBA championship ever in 1979.

From the time he showed up in Seattle, and we got to watch him perform his wizardry on the court, Luke, Kenny, and I always fought over who got to wear number 19. Those two argued that it should be one of them, since the names Luke and Kenny combine to make Lenny, so I had to settle for number 14, the number he wore as an All-American at Providence College.

Three years later, just before our sophomore year in high school, Luke, Kenny, and I met Mr. Wilkens at a basketball camp we went to on Whidbey Island. It turned out that as great as he was on the court paled in comparison to how amazing he was off the court. One of the classiest men to ever play the sport.

Lenny Wilkens was one of our heroes.

(Sadly, our love affair with the Sonics ended in 2008 when a lousy horse thief from Oklahoma City named Clay Bennett stole them, moved them, and renamed them. Now they go by the name *Thunder*, although here where they belong many refer to them as the *Thonics*.)

The spring of '69 rolled around, and wouldn't you know we had another professional sports team: our very own Major League Baseball team, the Seattle Pilots (again paying homage to the aviation industry in our area). Our basketball team was bad. But our baseball team was plain awful. Even though we had base stealing whiz "Tailwind" Tommy Harper, we won only 64 games and lost 98.

And to add insult to injury, at the conclusion of every game, as we were filing out of tiny, decrepit Sicks' Stadium, they would put a record on that would blast out over the loudspeakers:

"Go! Go! You Pilots. You proud Seattle team.

Go! Go! You Pilots. Go out and make a dream."

Which wouldn't have been that bad, except that midway through the season the record developed a scratch and began to skip. So after another loss we would have to endure:

"Go! Go! You pilots … you Pilots … you Pilots … you Pilots" … scratch, crackle, scratch … *"You proud Seattle team."*

(Sadly, another horse thief, this time a used car salesman from Milwaukee named Bud Selig, stole our Pilots after only one year and turned them into *Brewers*. What the heck kind of name is that for a professional sports team?!)

But the good news in the spring of '69 was that seventh graders were allowed to play school baseball. So Kenny and I proudly took our places on the Lewis & Clark Junior Varsity baseball team along with several other seventh graders and the eighth graders who weren't quite advanced enough to make the varsity. Only one seventh grader made the varsity: Luke Daisy, of course. Later we found out he was the first seventh grader to play varsity baseball at any of the Bonney Flats junior highs.

Now 5-foot-10 and 160 pounds, Luke certainly did not look like the youngest player on the team. The coach was our former third grade teacher, wonderful Mr. Stokes, who was as great of a coach as he was a teacher. And he certainly had no difficulty recognizing Luke's amazing ability, making him the leadoff hitter and starting shortstop.

Our first game was at Harrison Junior High, facing the big bully Bruce Junkers himself. Bruce may have been a misanthropic mutant muttonhead (Kenny's term, of course), but he was 6-foot-2, 190 pounds, and was just about to turn 16 (his dad held him out of school for a year so he would be older than those in his grade). And he could throw a baseball very, very fast.

Luke stepped in to lead off the game, batting right handed against the big lefty. Bruce looked in and glared at the boy who always seemed to be getting the best of him. His first pitch, a blazing fastball, was aimed right at Luke's head.

Luke reacted quickly, like he always did, and hit the ground as the ball sailed inches over his head. He popped back up and got right into his stance as if it was no big deal. Junkers got the ball back and sneered at Luke as if to say, "What're you gonna do about it, punk?"

He found out pretty quickly.

His next pitch was a fastball, high and away. Luke drove it into the gap in right center and cruised into third base with a stand-up triple.

Backing up third, Junkers got the ball back and as he walked past Luke he said, "You lucky piece of dirt." Only he didn't say "dirt," he said something more vulgar.

"Hey, watch your mouth," Luke responded. "Why don't you just shut up and pitch?"

"Oh yeah," Junkers said. "Are you gonna make me?"

"Gee, I thought maybe hitting that triple would shut you up. I guess I was wrong."

Junkers just glared and fumed.

"Oh, and if I were you, I wouldn't throw that change-up anymore," Luke continued.

"That wasn't a change-up, you idiot, that was a fastball," Junkers replied, not smart enough to pick up on the insult.

"What?!" Luke said, feigning shock. "That was your fastball?"

Now Junkers caught on, and I believe the smoke pouring out of his ears was visible for all to see.

The problem with being over-the-top angry is that it usually causes you to make mistakes. That was certainly the case when Junkers tried to pick off Luke three times, the third throw sailing high and wide, allowing Luke to walk home easily (it was actually more of a mosey or sashay).

Luke came to bat again in the third inning, and again Junkers' first pitch fastball just missed his head. His second pitch was also a fastball, and it was aimed right for Luke's ankles. Luke managed to dodge that pitch as well, but Coach Stokes had seen enough.

"Hey, hey, hey," he hollered, coming out of the dugout and approaching the home plate umpire. "Are you going to just let him stand out there and take target practice at our batter?"

"There's nothing I can do," replied the umpire.

"Of course there is. You can run him out of the game. Everybody here knows he's throwing at him on purpose."

"You don't know that for sure."

Coach Stokes just shook his head in disbelief, and headed over to their coach.

"Are you gonna do something about this, or just let this happen?" he asked.

Their coach just shrugged. "I guess maybe the ball is slippery," he said.

So Coach Stokes headed back to the dugout, giving Junkers the evil eye as he walked past. Junkers just gave it his old bully sneer.

Sure enough, his next pitch, another fastball, hit Luke right in the middle of the back. Luke dropped his bat and trotted to first. It had to hurt, but he was not about to give Junkers the satisfaction of looking like he was in any pain.

Our next batter was our Little League World Series hero, Gary Radliffe, and a strange thing happened when he swung at the first pitch. The bat slipped out of his hand and flew end over end right at the mound, striking Junkers in the left leg.

"Oops. Sorry," he said, retrieving his bat.

Our next batter was another of our World Series stars, pitcher Mike Monroe, and wouldn't you know, the bat slipped out of his hands as well. This one struck Junkers in the side.

Now it was their coach's turn to come out of the dugout yelling. "You better put a stop to this," he shouted at Coach Stokes.

"Sorry," he answered. "I guess maybe our bats are slippery."

Finally the umpire realized that things had gotten out of hand and he warned both sides. No more hit batsmen and no more flying bats, or that team would forfeit.

We scored two more runs to take a 3-0 lead into the bottom of the seventh and final inning, when Junkers came to bat with two outs. Coach Stokes strolled to the mound and took the ball from Mike, who had pitched a masterpiece, and called Luke in from shortstop. Coach said a few words to them, and then the two of them switched positions.

Now it was Luke's turn to stand there on the mound, ball in hand, smiling in at the bully who had fired missiles at him time after time. Poor Bruce did not care for this turn of events, and he was visibly shaking. The problem, I realized, was that if Luke hit him we would have to forfeit the game. I knew that Luke would never do that to his teammates, even if revenge would be sweet.

Bruce's tiny brain did not process that, however, and I'm sure he was anticipating great pain.

Luke was not a pitcher, but he could throw a baseball with a lot of velocity. He wound up and rifled in his pitch.

And it headed right for Bruce's head. Bruce let out a scream, flipped his bat in the air, and hit the ground hard. Sadly, the bat came down and landed right on his helmet.

Poor Bruce had no way of knowing that Luke could also throw a really good curveball. So while his life was flashing before his eyes, Luke's pitch was curving and dropping gently over the plate.

"Stee-rike one," the umpire yelled.

There was plenty of laughter, Luke and Mike switched positions again, and Mike fired two fastballs past Junkers to end the game and add another item in what was becoming a long list of humiliations for poor Bruce Junkers.

Chapter 27

<u>Summer of '69</u>

"We are all faced with a series of great opportunities brilliantly disguised as impossible situations." – Charles Swindoll

If ever there was a year to make you feel like all things were possible, to shoot for the stars, the sky's the limit, you can do anything if you set your mind to it, never say die, and every other inspirational cliche ̄, 1969 was it.

In January "Broadway" Joe Namath and the New York Jets of the upstart American Football League did what almost everyone thought was impossible: they beat the mighty Baltimore Colts of the National Football League, 16-7, to win Super Bowl III. The Colts, who lost just once all year and won the NFL championship, 34-0, were 18-point favorites. The Jets lost three times and barely won the AFL title, and their quarterback would go on to do commercials for panty hose.

People called it the biggest upset since a shepherd boy named David used his slingshot to fell the giant Goliath in the Valley of Elah several thousand years earlier. The odds on that battle were not published, but I'm pretty sure Jerusalem bookmakers had the Philistine as a prohibitive favorite.

Good news for the Colts: losing did not result in decapitation. Goliath – not so fortunate. Hey, it was a different time.

And then in the fall of that year, the New York Mets shocked the world by beating the mighty Baltimore Orioles and winning the World Series. The Lovable Losers had transformed into the Miracle Mets. In their eighth year in existence, not only had the

Mets never had a winning record, but they had never even finished higher than 9th place. Meanwhile the Orioles, with four future Hall of Famers, had won 109 games that year, and were about as invincible as … well, the Colts. Or Goliath.

It was a great year to be a sports fan in New York. Not so much in Baltimore. The Mets won 4 games to 1.

We tucked those two great underdog stories into our subconscious for later use when we faced some pretty tough odds of our own. It never hurts to have some inspiration.

But of course the most inspiring thing to happen in 1969 had nothing to do with sports.

There are a few days in each of our lives, I believe, that are so indelibly imprinted on our minds and in our hearts that we remember exactly where we were and who we were with, even the sounds and smells, as well as all of the emotions. Sunday, July 20, 1969 was one of those days for millions of people, including Ellie, and the Cateere, Carew, and Daisy families, who were all piled into our living room to watch the miracle on live television.

Four days earlier Apollo 11 had blasted off from the Kennedy Space Center in Florida (launched by a Saturn V SA-506 rocket, Mark Daisy explained to us laymen), with Mission Commander Neil Armstrong, Command Module Pilot Michael Collins, and Lunar Module Pilot Edwin "Buzz" Aldrin.

On Sunday the lunar module *Eagle* separated from the command module *Columbia*, and Mr. Armstrong announced, "The *Eagle* has wings." A couple of hours later it landed on the moon, at a site called the Sea of Tranquility, and Mr. Armstrong announced to the world, "The *Eagle* has landed."

Cheers from us kids; tears of awestruck joy from the adults.

And then we all watched in silent wonder as Mr. Armstrong stepped out of the Eagle onto the step ladder and onto the surface of the moon, saying, "That's one small step for a man, one giant leap for mankind."

We listened as President Nixon made what he called "the most amazing phone call ever placed from the White House." He said, "For one priceless moment in the whole history of man, all the people on this earth are totally one: one in their pride in what you have done, and one in our prayers that you will return safely to Earth."

Mr. Aldrin, the second man to walk on the moon, said, "I'd like to take this opportunity to ask every person listening in, whoever and wherever they may be, to pause for a moment and contemplate these events and give thanks in his or her own way." Later we learned that Mr. Aldrin, a deeply religious man, had privately taken communion when the *Eagle* landed on the moon's surface.

Later we all walked outside and stared up at the moon on that clear summer night.

"Can you believe it?" I said. "There are people walking around up there."

"I know," dad answered. "I never would have thought it possible."

"I hope the moon people are friendly," Ellie added with a smile.

Mr. Daisy had the perfect verse, of course. "The heavens declare the glory of God. The skies proclaim the work of his hands." (Psalm 19:1)

"In the beginning You laid the foundations of the earth, and the heavens are the work of Your hands," Mr. Carew added. (Psalm 102:25)

Kenny, of course, had to add his two cents. "When I admire the wonders of a sunset or the beauty of the moon, my soul expands in the worship of the Creator," he said.

I looked at him in amazement. "Who said that?" I asked.

He looked at me like there was something wrong with me. "I did," he said. "Could you not hear me?" (Later we found out it was a quote from Gandhi.)

Johnny had the final word. "Daddy," he announced boldly, in words we could all understand. "Someday I'm going to live on the moon."

On this night, when all things seemed possible, exactly one year to the day after Johnny had won his gold medal at the first Special Olympics, that didn't sound at all crazy.

One of Luke's most amazing athletic feats occurred that summer of '69, although there were very few people to witness it.

We were playing a summer baseball game at McLaren Park in the Babe Ruth League for 13-15 year-olds. At 13 we were the youngest in the league, but of course Luke was still probably the best player in the league. I played left field because I was pretty fast and I could catch well, although I had a weak throwing arm. Any balls hit into the gap I would run down and then throw a short relay to Luke, our shortstop, who could peg one right on the money to third or home, as needed.

Our team, *Hoffman Construction*, made it to the league championship game against *Holland Jewelry*. With a match-up of our two Little League World Series pitching stars, William Botts for us and Mike Monroe for them, everyone figured it would be a low-scoring pitchers' duel.

Sure enough, the score was tied 0-0 in the bottom of the fifth when *Holland* got a runner to third base with two outs. The next batter hit a blooper to shallow left field. Luke turned and sprinted out while I ran as fast as I could in. I realized I wasn't going to get there in time, but I thought maybe, just maybe, my superhuman friend would make the catch.

Luke dove, got completely horizontal, and stretched out his glove as far as it would go. For a second I thought the ball would land barely in the webbing, but it dropped just an inch or two beyond his reach. Luke slid and the ball bounced into his glove as the runner crossed home plate.

But the base umpire, who had been screened by Luke's diving body, raised his thumb and hollered "Out!" Third out of the inning, no run. Only Luke and I saw that he hadn't made the catch. We made eye contact and he shook his head as we headed back towards the infield, with cheers erupting from our dugout and stands.

But Luke didn't head for the dugout. Instead he went right to the umpire and told him, "I didn't catch it. It hit the ground first."

The call was reversed, the run counted, the batter got to go to first, and the inning continued. And my esteem for Luke Daisy grew even more than if he had made the catch.

Later I told him, "Luke, you know I never would have told anybody that you didn't make that catch."

"I know," he said. "But you'd have always known."

"Would you have said anything if I hadn't seen it?"

"I hope so. I think so. Because I'd have always known, too.

"You know how our dads are always talking about character, and that what matters is doing the right thing even when it costs you, and when nobody's looking," he added. And then he shrugged, "Well, I guess maybe some of that stuff sunk in."

And so we headed to the top of the seventh and final inning behind, 1-0, but we rallied to tie it, and then I came up to bat with two outs and the bases loaded. It was the kind of situation all ballplayers dream of, and those dreams always end with a grand slam, fireworks and confetti, big kiss from a pretty girl, and picture on the cover of *Sports Illustrated*.

Instead, my bat felt really, really heavy, and I think my prayer sounded something like this: "Dear Lord, please let him walk me."

I watched the first pitch go by, a fastball right down the middle of the plate. Strike one.

I swung feebly and missed the second pitch, another fastball. Strike two.

I just knew another fastball was coming, and so I decided to swing and hope the ball would somehow, miraculously, hit my bat.

But sometimes players outsmart themselves. The pitcher knew I was thinking fastball, so he decided to throw a curve.

And sometimes when 15-year-old boys try to throw a curveball, the ball doesn't curve. It just spins. And that's what happened. The ball started at my head and stayed at my head. I didn't react quickly enough, and as I started to duck the ball caromed off my helmet. Hit By Pitch. Possible game-winning RBI.

It didn't really hurt since it was an off-speed pitch, although my ears were ringing a little bit. I was pretty sure I hadn't suffered any brain damage, although I did question that hypothesis a few years later when I began trying to figure out calculus.

And so I trotted to first base. No fireworks or confetti, and no pretty girl kisses, but I was a slightly wounded hero nevertheless.

In the bottom of the seventh inning their first two hitters went out, and their third hitter hit a sky-high, towering pop foul down third base, just past our dugout, heading for the 8-foot chain-link fence that separated in-play from out-of-play. From my viewpoint in leftfield I could see that the ball was going to land just on the other side of the fence. I don't know how Luke could tell that from his position at shortstop.

But he took off at a sprint for the fence, dropped his glove just before he got there, and then transformed himself into Spiderman. With a running leap he hit the fence about three feet up and with his bare hands and cleats, scaled it in no time. At the top he reached over with his right hand and snagged the ball just as it cleared the fence. Third out. Game over. We win the championship.

And as Luke climbed back down the fence, there was a very strange reaction: silence. Dumbfounded silence. There were a few gasps, but really it took what seemed like a full minute before any of us truly realized what we had just seen. This was

Luke's level 3: "Holy cow did you see that? I can't believe what he just did!!!"

And then the cheering erupted. We had to be careful in our mauling of Luke, because his tricep was bleeding from where the top of the fence had poked through his skin. I'm not sure he really noticed, and he was smiling the whole time when dad stitched him up.

But I did have to remind everyone: "That was an amazing play, but let's not forget my heroic hit-by-pitch that really won the game for us."

I don't think I convinced anyone.

Chapter 28

Planning the Future

"The future belongs to those who believe in the beauty of their dreams." – Eleanor Roosevelt

"What do you want to be when you grow up?"

That's a question that pretty much every kid in America gets asked a couple hundred times in their life. When you're a little kid it's a pretty easy one: sheriff, cowboy, super hero, super model, rock star, all of the above.

By junior high the people asking are hoping for more reasonable answers, and sometimes you're left feeling like you'd better come up with something acceptable so that the adults in your life don't lose sleep over what might become of you when you enter the big, cruel, *real* world.

Kenny never worried. Sometimes he would tell people he wanted to be a mayonnaise salesman. "Everybody loves mayonnaise," he would explain. "And there will always be a need for sandwiches."

Sometimes he would say he wanted to be a garbage man, "because they only work one day a week."

Other times he would say, "I want to be an astronaut, and be the first man on the moon."

The questioner would furrow his brow and explain, "Ummm, we've already had a man on the moon."

"What?!" Kenny would exclaim. "I never heard about that?"

"Well, it was on TV, and in the newspapers."

"Okay then, I"ll be the first man on the sun," Kenny would say.

"Well that's impossible," the answer would come. "You'd burn up."

"Hey, I'm not stupid," Kenny would explain. "I'll go at night."

The subject came up one Saturday afternoon in the fall of our eighth grade year when the four of us – Luke, Kenny, Ellie, and I – were in our custom-made, luxury tree fort, courtesy of Matthew Daisy.

When Matthew returned from Vietnam he decided he would sleep better at night if he slept outside. "It's just easier for me to talk to God, and more importantly, to listen to God if I can look up and see the sky," he said. So he pitched a tent at first, but then quickly started working on a tree fort. And like everything he did, he set out to make it the best.

It was 6 feet off the ground in the Daisys' backyard deciduous oak tree, and to call it a tree fort is a gross mischaracterization. It wasn't even a treehouse. It was more of a tree mansion. It was 25-feet by 25-feet, and 7-feet high. He insulated the walls and the ceiling, which was made of corrugated metal, cut a 4x4 foot hole in the metal and filled it with clear, hard plastic for his sun roof so that he could always see the sky.

Then he installed gold shag carpeting (in honor of our beloved Sonics), and wired it for electricity, putting in an overhead light, miniature fridge, and a stereo. The final touches were a built-in bookcase, a table, and a bed.

The entrance included a mini trampoline that you could use to bounce to a platform two feet off the ground and then take the

5-step stairway to the entrance door, which was secured by a padlock. He also designed a pulley system to transport food, soda, books, games, etc. through the front window. There was also a separate back door, which opened to a covered yellow, plastic curly slide for an easy, fun exit.

Although there was no way to cook, and he would have to build a bathroom, I think Matthew planned to live there permanently. But then a funny thing happened. He fell in love and got married. And his new wife, bless her heart, said, "I love you Matthew, but I am not going to live in a tree."

And that is how the world's greatest tree fort – or as we called it "Oakwood Estates" – came to be our special gathering place.

So there we were in September of '69 when the subject came up of what we would be when we became adults. I wish I had it on tape.

"Luke, we know you're going to be a professional athlete," I said. "But which sport will you pick?"

"I don't know," he answered. "In the fall I think football, in the winter I think basketball, and in the spring I think baseball. I don't want to decide. At least not yet."

"I think someday you'll have to," I added.

"I don't know. Maybe I'll decide to do all three. What do you think about that?"

"Well, if anybody could do it, it would be you."

"How about you, Kenny Bear?" Ellie asked. "I know you'll be up front entertaining people for a living, but do you think it will be singing or telling jokes?"

"I'm with Luke," he responded. "I don't want to choose. I want to do both. I want to have an act where I sing and tell jokes."

"Well, if anybody could do it, it would be you," I confirmed.

"How about you, Mouse?" Kenny asked.

"Oh, I suppose I'll be a doctor, like my dad," I said.

"Nope," Luke said.

"What do you mean 'nope'?"

"You're not going to be a doctor, Mouse."

"Oh, really? What am I going to be?"

"You're going to be President of the United States."

I laughed. "Yeah, right."

"Hey, I'm serious," Luke continued. "Don't you get it, Mouse? You're the chosen one. You're the smartest and the kindest one of all. You're the one. I think it's your destiny."

I didn't know what to say. My friend had left me speechless.

"Does that mean," I finally said, "that you will all call me Mr. President? You know, if I still associate with you commoners."

"I will still call you Mikey Bear," Ellie answered.

"And I will call you Mr. Mouse," Kenny said.

"Hey," Ellie added. "Since Mouse isn't going to be a doctor, maybe I will be."

"Definitely," Luke concurred. "I'll even let you give me my shots."

"The main thing," I said, "is that we all have to do something that makes the world a better place. Like our parents."

"Ummm, I know that's true for all of your parents, but not mine," Ellie said a little sadly. "My parents haven't made anything better."

There was a moment of silence while we all thought about that.

"What are you talking about?" Kenny replied eventually. "Your parents gave us *you*!"

Luke and I looked at Kenny and nodded, and I was thinking what I often did when Kenny spoke: I wish I had said that. Ellie looked down, smiled, and managed to croak out, "Thanks, Hoppy Bear."

"You're welcome," Kenny shrugged. "Just don't ever tell anybody I said something nice to a girl."

"Being a doctor or being the president can definitely make the world a better place," Luke said, "but I don't see how being a professional athlete does. So what if I can hit a baseball a long way."

"Yeah, or being an entertainer," Kenny added. "How does that help?"

"Don't you see?" I answered. "They're going to pay you guys a ton of money for what you do. Luke, some professional baseball players make over $100,000. And Kenny, do you know how much all those guys on *Laugh-In* make?"

"No, do you?" he answered.

"No. But I'm sure it's a lot."

"Yeah, but Mouse, I don't care about the money," Luke said.

"But don't you get it? That's where you can make a difference, make the world a better place, by what you do with all that money," I explained. "For example, you could build hospitals."

"Yeah, and hire me," Ellie interjected.

"Yes," I went on. "And help feed starving people. And support missionaries, and orphanages, and the Red Cross, and the Salvation Army. Stuff like that."

"And build schools and homes for mentally retarded kids," Luke added with enthusiasm.

"And," I added for good measure, "support my presidential campaign."

"Whoa, hold on a second," Kenny said. "I'm not supporting your presidential campaign until I hear your platform. I have to know what's in it for me."

"Okay," I responded. "Here's what my first campaign speech might sound like: 'One time my friend Kenny Carew pooped his pants jumping off a 10-foot diving platform at Lincoln Lake.' How does that sound?"

Kenny just stared at me, open-mouthed.

Finally he answered. "How much are you going to need? Name your price."

Chapter 29

<u>Eighth Grade</u>

"Clowns to the left of me, jokers to the right, here I am stuck in the middle with you." – Gerry Rafferty (Stealers Wheel)

In September of 1969, just as we started eighth grade, one of the great movies of all time, *Butch Cassidy and The Sundance Kid*, hit the big screen. Although there were some fine actors in the film in smaller roles (Katharine Ross, Cloris Leachman, Strother Martin, Sam Elliott), it really was a movie about two people: Butch and Sundance, Paul Newman and Robert Redford. Those two so dominated the screen and the action, that it was easy to forget any of the others in the picture.

Being in eighth grade in a seventh-through-ninth grade junior high is kind of like being one of the actors in *Butch Cassidy and The Sundance Kid* **not** named Paul Newman or Robert Redford: overlooked. All of the attention was focused on the poor little seventh graders, trying to survive this quantum leap of maturity, and the king-of-the-hill ninth graders, perched on the edge of the big time: high school.

So we spent our school days being envious of the top dog ninth graders, and thankful that we were no longer the pipsqueak seventh graders.

Eighth graders in those days played junior varsity football and basketball, while the varsity teams were reserved for ninth graders. No exceptions. It didn't matter that Luke was the strongest, fastest, and best athlete in the school, even the whole district, he would be playing JV.

And that was good news for Kenny and me, who probably wouldn't have been good enough to beat out the older kids for a varsity spot. We got another year of being Luke's teammates.

At his summer physical Luke measured 6-feet, 180 pounds, and certainly did not look like a 13-year-old. He played quarterback on offense and middle linebacker on defense, kind of an odd combination. He was also our punter and punt returner, kicker and kick returner. And when we'd get way ahead, which was almost every game, the coach would put someone else in to do the kicking, and Luke would become our long snapper. There really wasn't much he couldn't do on the football field, although you would not have wanted to stand by him during the playing of the national anthem. Poor Mrs. Daisy would just cringe whenever Luke tried to sing.

In football that year Luke had two fairly significant advantages: nobody could tackle him, and nobody could block him. Johnny was one of the team managers, and before every game he would say to his brother, "Dohna hurem, Wookie." (Don't hurt them, Lukie.)

Fortunately, Luke was not inclined to inflict any injury on the smaller guys he was up against, and we had a coach who recognized that he was far superior to all of our opponents; that it was more important to let all of the boys play a significant amount ("Some of whom may not ever play after this year," he would point out) than it was to win games by 40 or 50 points.

Our coach was a very interesting man named Curt Hale. Coach Hale liked football, but his true passion was history. He loved teaching history: bringing the past alive for his students, helping us realize how we got to where we were, and how much we owed to the great men responsible. I used to think there was something wrong with our school clocks, because they moved so slowly during boring Mr. Capnick's science class, and so unbelievably fast during Mr. Hale's history class.

Even during football practice he would incorporate history lessons. If he was coaching defensive linemen how to get around blocks, he might launch into the story of the 1948-49 Berlin Airlift where the United States and our allies flew 9,000 tons of supplies every day into West Germany to overcome the Soviet blockade of that great city.

If he was talking about the importance of the rush, he might digress and talk about the California Gold Rush of 1848, which occurred just weeks after the Treaty of Guadalupe Hidalgo officially transferred ownership of that state from Mexico to the United States. "Timing is everything," he would say.

And if we were focusing on defense, he would likely launch into his passionate praise of the Royal Air Force in their defense against Germany in the Battle of Britain. "Never in the field of human conflict was so much owed by so many to so few," he would quote the great Winston Churchill.

In fact, his pre-game speeches were filled with great quotes from the likes of Churchill and Lincoln.

"I need you to give me your blood, your toil, your sweat, and your tears," he would encourage. "We're all in this together. A house divided against itself cannot stand. When we leave that field, let all those fans look at us and say that this was their finest hour."

We loved him.

So here is how the games would usually go: on our first possession Luke would run one in for a touchdown. On their first possession Luke would either intercept or cause a fumble.

On our second possession Luke would run one in for another touchdown. And then, no more running for Luke, only passing.

That was good news for Kenny and me, who were the two wide receivers. That summer we had spent a lot of time running pass routes with Luke, perfecting our patterns and our timing. Sometimes we were Don Meredith throwing to Bob Hayes and Lance Rentzel. Sometimes we were Bart Starr throwing to Boyd Dowler and Carroll Dale. Or Joe Willie Namath to George Sauer and Don Maynard. Or Daryle "The Mad Bomber" Lamonica to Warren Wells and Fred Biletnikoff.

We may not have been as good as our imaginations, but we got to be a pretty fair passing combination. That meant that both Kenny and I got to experience the joy of scoring touchdowns, and get a glimpse of the glory that Luke experienced on a regular basis.

So we went undefeated in football, and then undefeated in basketball. Luke's domination in basketball was surpassed only by his determination to keep getting better. It was around this time that he stopped taking the bus to school and would ride his bike or run the three miles. In practice he would wear a weighted jacket to improve his stamina and leg strength.

In the middle of the season, after the calendar had switched over to January, Luke called Kenny and Ellie and me on a Saturday morning and told us to get over to his house because he had something he wanted to show us. We would probably have been headed that way eventually, but this was before our cereal and Bugs Bunny cartoons. It was a few days before his birthday, so we figured it had something to do with a new present.

Instead we found him in his driveway with a basketball, already warmed up and shooting. Kenny and I arrived together first and asked him what was up. He just smiled and said, "Wait for Ellie." A few minutes later she rolled in on her bike. "Good morning, cubbies," she said. "What's so important that I didn't get to finish my *Cap'n Crunch*?"

"How can you eat that stuff, Ellie?" Kenny asked. "It tears up the roof of my mouth."

"I guess I'm just tougher than you," she answered with a smile.

"Why would you want to eat anything other than *Cocoa Krispies*?" I interjected. "No pain, and pretty soon you've got your own bowl of chocolate milk."

"No way, man," Kenny said. "*Froot Loops* are where it's at."

After a few more minutes where arguments were made for *Frosted Flakes* ("They're grrrrrreat!"), *Sugar Crisp* ("Can't get enough of that *Sugar Crisp*"), *Lucky Charms* ("They're magically delicious"), and *Trix* ("*Trix* are for kids"), even a half-hearted case for *Alpha Bits* ("They may taste like cardboard, but you can spell stuff"), Luke finally said, "Are you three gourmet food critics through? I want to show you something."

"Oh yeah," I said. "Sorry. What is it?"

"Watch this," he said.

And with that he dribbled his red, white, and blue A.B.A. basketball to the end of the driveway, paused for a few seconds to tighten the laces on his PF Flyers, and then raced full speed towards the basket. I realized what I was about to see, but I could hardly believe it. I can still picture it, almost as if it was in slow motion.

On January 17, 1970, four days before he turned 14, on the 10-foot basket in his driveway, Luke Theophilus Daisy dunked a basketball.

The three of us stood there in stunned silence. You would think that by this time there would be nothing he could do that would surprise us. But he kept on surprising us.

"Pretty cool, huh?" Luke said.

Yes! Definitely very cool!

We were hoping Luke would get a chance to dunk in a game, although we didn't even know if it would be legal. The NCAA had recently outlawed dunking in college basketball games in a misguided effort to take away the advantage of the great Lew Alcindor (now Kareem Abdul-Jabbar) and other giants in the game. The Washington Interscholastic Athletic Association, which governed high school basketball in our state, soon followed suit. But nobody seemed to know if it applied to junior high games – *junior varsity junior high games for that matter* – I think, because, nobody really thought it could become an issue.

Luke had a way of forcing people to change their thinking.

Chapter 30

The Rivalry

"First they ignore you, then they laugh at you, then they fight you. Then you win." – Gandhi

Just east of Bonney Flats, nestled in the foothills of the Cascades, was the city of Waterton. Although it was nearly twice the size of Bonney Flats, the city still had just one high school. With over 3,000 students, Waterton High School was far and away the largest in the state.

Consequently, they were one of the most dominant high schools in sports, especially football and basketball. For years the Rebels had ruled the roost in our Hanahan County Conference. Every league title had to go through Waterton, and they would not go down without a fight. Often literally. With a large population of loggers, farmers, and miners, their unspoken mantra seemed to be: "We're tougher than you are." And very few came along to challenge that premise.

Luke's first challenge to that came in the final basketball game of our eighth grade year. Since we were the JV team, we would sit in the stands and watch the ninth grader's Varsity game, and then play our game immediately following.

Well, our ninth grade team was mediocre at best, and Waterton's was undefeated, winning every game by huge margins. For some reason, on this afternoon, their coach, Mr. Justin Case, decided to see how much he could win by. So he left his starting lineup in and kept the full court press on, even as his lead increased from 10 to 20 to 30 to 40 points. Apparently his goal was total humiliation of our guys. I'm not really sure if it was personal, or if he was just an egotistical jerk and a bully. (I think probably he wasn't loved enough as a child.)

And if there was one thing Luke couldn't stand, it was bullies. So halfway through the fourth quarter he stood up in the stands and started to boo loudly, and then heckle their coach.

"Come on coach," he yelled. "Does this make you feel like a real man? Boo. You ever hear of a thing called sportsmanship? Boo. Bush league. Total bush league."

Coach Case was not used to being challenged, especially by a kid, and he turned red with anger. "Sit down and shut up," he yelled at Luke. Luke ignored him, and soon the rest of us had joined him in the booing.

So he marched over to our coach, Mr. Peavey, and jabbed a finger in his chest. "You'd better get your kids under control," he demanded.

There are a lot of ways to bring a man to his knees, but few are quicker than grabbing his extended index finger and bending it backwards. Coach Peavey, basically a gentle man with a solid knowledge of self-defense techniques, did just that.

"Don't ever jab your finger at me again," he said to the kneeling, groaning coach. "And don't ever talk to any of my players again."

The referees hustled over and separated the two coaches. The game resumed, and shortly thereafter Waterton walked off the court with a 99-36 victory. But their coach was not as pleased as you'd think he might be after a 63-point victory, and he glared up at Luke as he stomped out of the gym.

"Hey coach," Luke called after him. "What goes around comes around. See you next year."

Sure enough, we played Waterton Junior High the final game of our ninth grade year. This time we were undefeated (after going undefeated in football again), while Waterton had the mediocre team. We had won all of our games comfortably, with Coach Peavey playing all the kids and making sure we never ran up the score.

And Luke did something remarkable that season. I know that sort of goes without saying, but I mean remarkable even for him. Partly because of his love for Lenny Wilkens, and partly because he just always wanted to keep getting better, he would play half the games left-handed (like Lenny) and half the games right-handed. If you didn't know better, you'd have been hard-pressed to tell which was his natural hand (right). He wanted to win as much as anybody I ever knew, but he didn't care how many points he scored, or by how much we won.

Except for that last game against Waterton. I had never seen him so fired up, so intense.

"Listen to me," he said through gritted teeth in the locker room before the game. "We are going to play this game harder than we've ever played. We are going to dive for every loose ball, fight for every rebound, play like our lives depended on it. Don't even let them get the ball across half court.

"Remember what their coach did to our guys last year, how he went out of his way to humiliate them," he added. "Now it's payback time. Now we get even. Now we teach a bully a lesson."

Luke walked over and smiled at Coach Case before the opening tip. "Remember me?" he asked. "Well, we've been waiting for you."

Coach Case didn't say anything, but it looked as though he might have had four or five lemons for lunch.

The game started, and you have never seen a team play any harder than the Lewis & Clark Pathfinders did that day. Diving, trapping, taking charges, offensive rebounds. All five guys flying around the court, like our lives depended on it, just like Luke suggested.

At the end of the first quarter it was 22-0. Waterton had called two timeouts, and during both of them we stayed out on the court, ready to continue. It was Coach Peavey's suggestion.

The second quarter was more of the same, and we went into halftime ahead 45-1. Their only point came on a technical foul shot, after Luke had stolen a pass and soared in for a slam dunk. The referee blew his whistle, conferred with his partner, and then decided that it was, indeed, against the rules for a junior high kid to dunk a basketball.

Coach Case stormed into his locker room at halftime, followed by his shell-shocked, dejected players. In our locker room, Luke addressed the team. "Well done, guys," he said. "I think we proved our point."

Coach Peavey agreed, and decided we would play our substitutes the rest of the way, with no more full court press. But it didn't really matter, because Coach Case refused to bring his team back out for the second half. They quit. Got on the bus and drove back to Waterton.

Later, in a hearing with his school board, Coach Case tried to convince them that he did it because he was afraid for his team's safety. They didn't buy it, and he was suspended from coaching his team the following year. You'd think he might have learned a lesson in all that, but we found out later that, in fact, he did not.

Chapter 31

<u>The Dance</u>

"Man cannot discover new oceans unless he has the courage to lose sight of the shore." – Andre Gide

An undefeated ninth grade baseball season was pretty much a foregone conclusion, which meant we completed our junior high years undefeated in all three sports. It was getting hard to remember the last time we lost a game. Ah, the joy of being Luke Daisy's teammate.

But there were a couple of noteworthy occurrences during that final season.

When you play alongside a great player day in and day out, competing with him in games and against him in practice, some of his greatness often wears off on you. It's an old adage but true: great players make those around them better. That was certainly the case for me.

Luke had been moved to third in the batting order, and I batted second, which meant that I got to see an awful lot of pitches right down the middle of the plate because they didn't want to walk me and have someone on base when it was Luke's turn to hit. At the same time my skinny body had started to fill out. When I stood in front of the mirror without my shirt on and flexed (which, I have to admit, I did almost every morning), you could truly see some muscle definition. I mean, you had to look pretty close, but trust me, it was there.

(I made the mistake of leaving the door open during one of my Saturday morning flexing sessions and Kenny happened to walk by and catch a glimpse of me posing. He called me Charles Atlas for a month.)

Anyway, the thing is, I got to be a pretty good hitter. And in the final game of the season, an 8-3 win over Harrison Junior High, I hit two home runs, one of them a grand slam.

But even more amazing that game was that Luke struck out. All four times he batted. We had never even seen him strike out once, let alone accomplish a "Golden Sombrero" for four straight whiffs.

As thrilled as I was about the two homers, I was still mystified by Luke's struggles at the plate that day. But he was not one to pout and rob me of my joy.

"Way to go, Mouse!" he yelled in the dugout after the game, engulfing me in a giant bear hug. "You were flat out amazing today. Nice going, superstar."

Later we went for pizza at Wimpy's, and I could tell Luke was not himself.

"Are you thinking about the strikeouts today?" I asked.

"No."

"Still, that was really weird. What happened?"

"I don't want to make excuses," he said, "but I could not concentrate. My mind was a million miles away. I can't stop thinking about something."

"What is it?"

Luke looked down, took a deep breath, and then looked back up at me.

"My mom says I have to go to the ninth grade dance," he finally said. "And I have to ask a girl."

Every school year at Lewis & Clark Junior High ended with a traditional dance in the gymnasium, complete with full decorations, strobe lights, refreshments, chaperones, and a disc jockey playing all of the latest hits. In the spring of 1971 that meant we'd be gyrating to, among others, Three Dog Night (*"Joy to the World"*), The Rolling Stones (*"Brown Sugar"*), Daddy Dewdrop (*"Chick-a-Boom"*), Lobo (*"Me and You and a Dog Named Boo"*), and The Buoys (*"Timothy,"* without doubt the greatest song about cannibalism ever written). Our dance, titled *"Put Your Hand in the Hand"*, which was a hit song by the one-hit wonder group Ocean, was coming up in three weeks.

"Why does she say you have to go?" I asked.

"Oh, she said something about expanding my horizons, learning to appreciate the finer things in life, not being so one-dimensional, blah blah blah."

"So why is that such a big deal? So you ask a girl to the dance." It was strange to see my amazing friend feeling nonplussed about anything.

"Well for one thing, Einstein, I don't know how to dance," he said. "And for another, I don't know how to talk to girls. How am I supposed to just walk up to a girl and ask her if she wants to go the dance with me?"

"Well, number 1, Mr. Strikeout," I answered sarcastically, "you don't need to know how to dance. No boy our age knows how to dance. You just kind of flail your arms around and move your feet around to the rhythm. Besides, nobody will even be watching you. Everybody just watches the girls. They know what they're doing. They practice in front of the mirror all the time I think.

"And second, why don't you just ask Ellie to the dance? You know how to talk to her."

Luke looked at me like I was crazy.

"You think I should ask Ellie?" he asked incredulously. "You really think that I am the one who should ask Ellie?"

"Well, yeah, why not?" I answered.

He just shook his head sadly.

"You know, Mouse, for being the smartest person around, sometimes you sure are a dunce," he said.

"What are you talking about?"

"You know how you look at Ellie with those goo goo eyes when she doesn't see you and you think nobody else sees you?"

"I don't do that."

"Yes you do. Well, Mr. Denial Guy, she looks at you the same way when you're not looking."

"She does?"

Again the sad shaking of his head.

"Of course she does. Now stop being a doofus and ask her to the dance."

I could hardly believe what I was hearing. Was it really true? All of a sudden I felt like I could fly.

"Okay, I will," I said finally. "But you can't call me a doofus if you aren't even brave enough to invite someone. So who do you want to invite?"

"I don't know," he said. But after a short hesitation he added, "Maybe Katie Thomas."

"Really? Katie Thomas, huh?" I smiled. "Luke and Katie, sitting in a tree …"

"Shut up, Mouse!"

"All right. Sorry. How come Katie?"

"Well, she sits next to me in Geometry, and she smells good. And she's smart and she's nice and I think she's the prettiest girl in the school."

"You think she's prettier than Ellie?" I asked.

"Ellie doesn't count," he said. "Plus, I don't think Katie would laugh at my dancing."

"Well, those are all pretty good reasons, Luke," I said. "Now all you have to do is work up the courage to ask her. I can pretty much guarantee you that she will say yes."

So the next day I asked Ellie to the dance. She said yes, and I was glad I was on the ground floor because I think I really might have leaped right out of a second floor window, I was that sure that I could fly. Kenny was going with Karen Paulsen, who just happened to be the female version of himself. They were the two star singers in the choir and often the leads in the school plays.

Now it was up to Luke to ask Katie, and I told him he'd better hurry because somebody else would probably ask her if he waited too long. Meanwhile, Ellie and I had told Katie that Luke was going to ask her, and she assured us that she would say yes.

So Luke shuffled up to us a few days later with a piece of paper in his hand.

"How does this sound?" he asked and began to read from the paper. "Dear Katie, I would be honored if you would accompany me to the school dance. Although I don't know how to dance, I will try not to embarrass you. Also, I tend to perspire heavily when I get nervous, but I will wear lots of deodorant so that hopefully I won't smell bad. If your answer is no, I will understand. If your answer is yes, that would be great. We can go with Mouse & Ellie, Kenny & Karen. They are all good at talking so I think we would have a good time. Sincerely, Luke."

We just stared at him, open mouthed.

"Wow!" Ellie finally said.

"You think it sounds okay?" Luke asked.

"Did Johnny help you write that?" Kenny responded. Luke gave him the evil eye.

"Luke, you're not planning to send that or read it to her, are you? Because you can't ask Katie to the dance with written correspondence," I explained.

"Of course not, you knucklehead," he answered. "I'm going to memorize it."

We just had to laugh at our poor, pitiful, wonderful friend who was facing, perhaps for the first time, something that did not come easy to him. So he memorized his invitation, and sure enough Katie said yes. She actually thought it was sweet.

And so we danced. Well, the best we could. It was just hard to figure out what to do with our arms. Luke looked like he was dribbling a basketball, trying to incorporate some basketball moves into his dancing. Kenny said that I looked like a man who was trying to find his car keys.

I noticed Luke watching Katie dance with a sense of awe, as if he was thinking, "Wow! How does she do that?" I had to laugh at the irony, since we often thought the same thing about Luke when we were out on the court or the field.

He even managed to talk to Katie. "Would you like some punch?" he asked. Hey, it was a start.

Luke sat out the slow songs (including *If*, by Bread, and *Rainy Days & Mondays*, by The Carpenters), but I have to admit, I think I enjoyed those the most. I remember thinking Ellie must be holding me down, because I really felt like I was just going to float away.

Being able to fly. Now that's a good feeling. And as I danced one of those slow dances, a thought occurred to me: "I'm only 15 years old and this might be the happiest I will ever be in my whole life."

Well I've been wrong way too many times in my life to keep track, but this might have been the fastest that I ever found out that I was way wrong. Because in just a few minutes they announced the winners of the voting for King and Queen of the dance.

The Queen was the beautiful and wonderful Ellie Fent. I think the only one surprised about that was Ellie herself.

And then they announced the King. I wasn't sure if it was going to be Kenny or Luke. Either one would have made for a perfect ending of this perfect night.

But it was neither. Instead, in May of 1971, the ninth grade class of Lewis & Clark Junior High selected as its King the most kind-hearted, loving boy any of us knew.

Johnny Daisy.

That night I think we all felt like we could fly.

Chapter 32

Summer of '71

"If it could only be like this always – always summer, the fruit always ripe." – Evelyn Waugh

Do you remember a time in your life when everything seemed perfect? When your days were full of fun and laughter. When the future was bright for you and all of your friends. When the sky always seemed to be blue. When you woke up carefree, and went to bed with a wonderful feeling of peaceful, contented, exhaustion.

That's what the summer of 1971 was like for us.

We spent a week at basketball camp, where we met the great Lenny Wilkens.

We spent a week at Bible camp, studying the great book of Romans. *("If God is for us, who can stand against us? Who shall separate us from the love of Christ? In all things we are more than conquerors through Him who loved us.")*

We were thrilled when one of our heroes, the great Bob Gibson of the St. Louis Cardinals, pitched a no-hitter against the eventual World Series champion Pittsburgh Pirates.

We played in a summer baseball league and a summer basketball league. We played touch football on the school playground, and field hockey in our back yard.

We played and played.

And we looked forward to the fall when we would officially become Paul Revere High School Minutemen.

Best of all, Ellie liked me. I mean she "like" liked me. All was right with the universe.

The problem with perfect is that it doesn't last.

One of Kenny's best gags was the prat fall, perfectly timed and flawlessly executed. He could enter a room and "accidentally" trip in a way that would have the unaware gasping. Sometimes he would do it, turn it into a somersault and just keep walking like nothing had happened. Sometimes he'd be holding food and when he tripped it would fly right to one of us for a saving catch. (Of course, we usually knew it was coming.) He practiced tripping on the basketball court with the ball in his hands and on the way down flipping it up underhand and having it go in the hoop. He could make the "trip shot" about two-thirds of the time.

The second week of August, not long before our sophomore school year was going to start, we were hanging out in our tree house, Oakwood Estates, after another long day of playing.

"Hey guys, I have to tell you something," Kenny said, sounding very serious.

Of course he started a lot of his crazy stories this way, so we didn't really know what to expect.

"There's something wrong with me," he said.

"Yeah, tell us something we don't know," Ellie responded.

Kenny looked at her and sort of half-smiled.

"No, I'm serious," he went on. "You know how I do my trip-and-fall gag? Well, sometimes I'm not doing it on purpose. There's something wrong with my legs or something. It's like my brain is forgetting to tell my muscles to work. And a lot of times I just feel exhausted. Maybe I have mono or something. I don't know."

We had noticed that Kenny had spent less time with us than usual that month. Sometimes he said he wanted to work on his music, and sometimes he said he just didn't feel up to it. And while he had been the fastest kid in the school (not counting Luke, of course), I noticed that I could now keep up with him. I just thought I was getting faster, but looking back, I could see that he was slowing down.

"Kenny, man, we got to get you checked out," I said. "I'll go talk to my dad right now."

"Yeah, for sure," Luke added. "Mikey's dad will figure this out. You'll be okay."

"Why didn't you tell us sooner, Kenny Bear?" Ellie asked.

"I don't know," he answered, looking down. "I just kept thinking it was a weird thing that would go away. But now it's been about a month since I noticed it."

We just shook our heads. We didn't know what to say.

Kenny looked up at us. "I'm kind of scared."

I think we all were.

Unfortunately, those fears were well-warranted.

After a long and painful process of blood tests and brain scans, poking, probing, and prodding, the diagnosis was that Kenny had a rare neurological disorder which was affecting the nerve cells responsible for controlling voluntary muscle movement.

It was called Amyotrophic Lateral Sclerosis.

Also known as ALS.

Also known as Lou Gehrig's Disease.

Our fast, funny friend, who brought so much joy and laughter into our lives, was headed for a very challenging life. Dad explained to us that the disease was progressive, irreversible, and untreatable. Kenny's sports days were over, most certainly he would spend most of his life in a wheelchair, and worst of all, his life expectancy would be cut way short.

In one quick flash our carefree lives came to a crashing halt. "It feels like we'll never smile again," I said.

As usual, we went to Mr. Daisy for some sort of understanding.

"I sure wish there were some easy answers," Luke's dad said sadly, "something I could say that would make this easier. But there isn't. It's just a really lousy thing that a great kid like Kenny, and a fantastic family like the Carews, have to go through something like this.

"The sad truth is that we live in a fallen world, where death and disease are everywhere, and nobody is exempt, no matter how wonderful they are," he continued. "But I do know this: God hasn't abandoned Kenny. He hasn't forgotten about him. He doesn't love him any less.

"I'm going to keep trusting God's promises, and that he has wonderful things ahead for Kenny. Remember what you guys just learned in the book of Romans this summer: 'We know that in all things God causes everything to work together for the good of those who love Him and are called according to His purpose.' We have to hold onto that."

I really wanted to believe that something good could come of this, and every day when I prayed for Kenny I also prayed that I would have more faith.

Wouldn't you know it was Kenny himself who cheered us up.

"I guess this makes me the luckiest man on the face of the earth, now that Lou Gehrig is dead," he said. He explained that his sisters who always picked on him were now being especially nice. And that the doctors said, as far as they could tell, he was the youngest person ever diagnosed with ALS. "So it looks like I'll make it into the Guinness Book of World Records even before Luke," he pointed out.

"But the truth is," he said, "I know these doctors are very sapient and dimistrious, but I'm pretty sure they're wrong about me. How could I possibly have Lou Gehrig's disease? I haven't hit a home run in my life."

He also told us, "I've written a song about this. Tell me what you think of the lyrics:

'If I ever lose my legs, I won't moan, and I won't beg. Cause if I ever lose my legs, I won't have to walk no more.' "

Of course we all recognized those lyrics from the recent Cat Stevens hit song *Moonshadow*. And so we did, after all, smile again.

"Seriously, guys," he said, "it's going to be okay. I really feel a peace about this. I know a lot of people are praying for me, and I know my family and you guys will always be there for me."

"You got that right," Luke nodded.

"And who knows? Maybe I'll surprise them all and never need a wheelchair."

We all nodded and smiled at our amazing friend.

"Well, if anyone can beat this, it's you," Ellie said, giving him a hug.

Finally, I asked: "*Sapient*?"

"It means having great wisdom. I just looked it up," Kenny explained.

"And *dimistrious*?"

"Yeah, I made that one up."

Chapter 33

High School Begins

"So I close my eyes to old ends, and open my heart to new beginnings." – Nick Frederickson

And so we started high school football practice, two weeks before school began, without our friend Kenny as a teammate. We tried to convince him to be the team manager, but he said he wanted to focus all of his spare time on his singing and acting. The football program's loss was more than made up for by the music and drama programs' gains. And if you didn't know better, you probably wouldn't be able to tell that something very serious was going on in his body. He moved a little slower and sometimes shuffled his feet, but he was still the quickest around with a joke and a smile.

At 15, Luke was now 6-foot-2 and 200 pounds of solid muscle as we began our sophomore year. (I had shot up to just a hair under 6-foot and 160 pounds of slightly discernable muscle.) Some of the thinking back in those days was that you had to be careful lifting weights because you could lose flexibility and speed. Luke made sure he did tons of stretching to go along with his weight lifting, so he was not only the strongest kid in our class, but still the fastest.

Now you would think that every high school football coach in America would be deliriously happy to have a player like Luke joining his program. Unfortunately, Coach Jeego of Paul Revere High School was not one of them.

Hugh Jeego had been the head football coach for 10 years at Revere H.S., where each season they won about half of their games. And each year he would explain that the only reason they didn't win more was because "these boys just weren't tough enough."

He had been an Army sergeant during the Korean War, and was always eager to tell people about his heroics overseas. (Years later it occurred to me that it wasn't the real war heroes who bragged about what they had done, just the pretenders.) Coach Jeego's offense was basically three plays: run the ball up the middle, run the ball to the left, and run the ball to the right. I believe he thought that the forward pass had been dreamed up by some hippie, communist, weirdo.

Mostly, he wanted everyone to know that this was his team, his program, and it was his way or the highway. He sure wasn't about to have any sophomore hot shot come in and grab the limelight.

"All right, listen up," he said at our first team meeting towards the end of summer. "Varsity and Junior Varsity kids will practice at 10 a.m. and 4 p.m. Sophomores will practice at 1 p.m." And after a bunch of other details he added, "Any questions?"

My guess is that rarely had anybody asked any questions, because he looked surprised when Luke raised his hand.

"What is it?" coach Jeego asked.

"What if you're a sophomore but you want to try out for the Varsity?" Luke asked.

"Sophomores don't play Varsity football here," coach answered curtly.

"Oh. Is that a league rule?"

"No. That's my rule. You got a problem with that?"

"No sir. I was just curious."

"So you think you're better than these junior and seniors, young man?"

"No sir. I just wanted to have the chance to try out and see."

"Well that's not gonna happen," coach Jeego said, now visibly upset. "And I'll tell you something else. If you don't stop challenging my authority, you'll never play Varsity football here. Do you understand that?"

Luke nodded. "Yes sir."

It was all kind of surreal. How Luke's simple question could be perceived by the coach as a challenge and get him so riled up was something we could not figure out.

And so Luke was relegated to the sophomore team as if he were just another sophomore, which he most certainly was not. It was unexpected but good news for me, as I had not anticipated being Luke's teammate this year. And it was very good news for our sophomore team coach, Mr. Rick Hermansen, who had just graduated from the University of Puget Sound and was in his first year of teaching and coaching.

But it was very, very bad news for the other sophomore teams in our league, who had to wonder why in the wide, wide world of sports this man-among-boys was playing against and destroying their teams.

In the fall of 1971 the Revere High School sophomore football team went 9-and-0. Luke scored 25 touchdowns, which included three kick returns, two punt returns, two interception returns, and a fumble return. He also passed for 20 more. I was on the receiving end of 12 of those TD passes, although to be honest, only one of them was a particularly nice catch. The others were just a matter of running fast, putting my hands out, and letting the ball fall into them.

Coach Jeego's varsity squad won 4 games and lost 5 (because "they just weren't tough enough.") They had 0 touchdown passes. At one point midway through the season, coach Hermansen approached coach Jeego and suggested that maybe, just maybe, he ought to reconsider his rule and move Luke up to the varsity. Coach Jeego threw him out of his office. I'm pretty sure he had grown quite tired of everybody – parents, other teachers and coaches, students, reporters - asking him why Luke was not playing on the varsity, but he was way too stubborn of a man to ever admit that he was wrong.

When the season was over and we turned in our equipment, Luke knocked on the door of the coaches' office to talk to coach Wagon, who was the varsity defensive coordinator but also the head basketball coach.

"First basketball practice is Monday after school, right coach?" Luke asked

"That's right, Luke," coach Wagon answered. "See you there."

"Coach," Luke continued, "do you have a rule against sophomores playing on the varsity?"

Coach Wagon kind of smirked, while coach Jeego sat in the background and gave Luke the stink eye.

"Why, no I don't have any such rule, Luke," coach Wagon said. "Best 12 players make the varsity, regardless of grade."

"Great," Luke nodded. "See you Monday."

It took about 15 minutes of the first basketball practice for everyone to realize that Luke was not only good enough to make the varsity, but was clearly going to be the best player on the team. In 1971 the average high school team in our parts had a couple of guards under 6-feet tall, a couple of forwards in the 6'2 range, and if you were lucky a center at 6'5 or 6'6. To have a 6-2 ½ guard, and one who could handle the ball flawlessly, was a real bonus. Coach Wagon couldn't stop smiling.

Charlie Wagon (his friends called him Chuck) was part Inuit and part Tlingit – back in those days we used the term Eskimo. He was raised in a tiny fishing village in western Alaska called Naknek, about 400 miles southwest of Anchorage on Bristol Bay. Raised by a deaf father, a fisherman, and a deaf mother, a lighthouse operator, Charlie was the only coach I ever knew who never once yelled. He never even raised his voice in anger, only when he needed to be heard above a crowd. I guess he learned fairly early that it didn't do much good to raise your voice. He also never swore, and he never argued with a referee, although one time I heard him whisper under his breath something about Mr. Magoo.

(Years later, however, I learned some sign language and figured out that he had, on occasion, spelled out some less-than-complimentary words to officials he didn't like. When I told him what I had figured out, he just smiled and shook his head. "Nah, you must have misread my hands," he said.)

Charlie grew up doing two things: working in the salmon canneries and playing basketball. He hated the first and loved the second. He wasn't very good at the one, but was fantastic at the other. At Bristol Bay High School he averaged 40 points a game, and then starred at the University of Alaska-Anchorage, where he may have been the only 5-foot-8-inch Most Valuable Player of the Great Northwest Athletic Conference.

At 30 he was the youngest head coach in our Hanahan County Conference, and still could play as though he was in his prime. He played in, and dominated, the Bonney Flats men's league games, which we would sometimes go to. Better yet, we got to watch Luke and him go at it, one-on-one, before and after practice. He was the quickest player we had ever seen, and we could see Luke getting even better just playing against him. (I didn't even realize that was possible.)

Charlie's basketball philosophy was pretty simple: play as hard as you can, don't play selfishly, and have fun. His Revere High School teams always seemed to win more games than they should, simply because of how much they hustled.

Coach Wagon loved kids, basketball, teaching, and coaching. The only thing he really seemed to hate was fish. Especially salmon.

We all loved him.

Luke was not the only sophomore to make varsity in our league, but he was for sure the only one to be named the captain of his team. Coach Wagon took him aside early and told him, "This is your team, Luke. You show them the way and take them where you want to go."

Still, Luke felt a little awkward about taking over, and was always afraid of shooting too much and appearing selfish. "These guys are seniors," he said of his teammates. "They've paid their dues. They deserve to get their shots."

What often happened was that Luke would drive to the hoop and then dish it off to a teammate, who would either fumble the pass or miss the open shot. Coach Wagon kept telling him, "Luke, it's not selfish if you're helping your team win."

After six games we were a respectable 4-and-2, with Luke averaging 12 points and 12 assists per game. (I say "we" although I was a proud member of the Junior Varsity team.)

Next up was a trip to The Woodshed.

Waterton High School had not lost a home basketball game in 5 years, and so their home gym came to be known as The Woodshed, where visitors would always take a beating. The rumors were that the referees for their home games were either former Waterton High School players, or else business owners in the city of Waterton. I'm not sure if either was correct, but I do know visiting teams did not seem to get a fair shake when they played there.

Waterton had won the league championship ten consecutive years, and came into the game with a perfect 6-and-0 record. They had three starters returning from last year's team, and were ranked fourth in the state. And while Luke was still early in his high school career, the legend of Luke Daisy had already spread throughout the region. Waterton was especially aware of him, after the way he had torched their ninth grade team and dirtbag coach, Justin Case, who, incidentally, was sitting at the scorer's table for this game.

The Woodshed was packed and loud when the game started. The Rebels controlled the tip off, worked the ball around and scored inside for a quick 2-0 lead, and then set up for their trademark full-court man-to-man press.

We inbounded the ball to Luke, and their all-league guard Frank Limadeer pretty much full body-blocked him and the ball out of bounds, with Luke crashing up against the gym wall. The referee, standing right there, signaled Waterton ball. No foul called.

Our guys just kind of stood there stunned, and then the same ref handed the ball to them to throw in before our guys were even ready. Luke was still on the ground as Waterton scored an easy basket. Still stunned, our players were just kind of standing around as the referee began his five-count for us to inbound the ball. Finally Luke gathered himself and called timeout.

Limadeer got up in Luke's face and sneered, "What do you think of that, hotshot?"

"Well, I think that's the only way you'll ever take the ball from me, is to foul me," Luke answered.

"Yeah, well there was no foul called."

"Everybody in this place knows you fouled me."

"Well guess what. There's more where that came from."

"Oh yeah? I guess we'll see about that," Luke finished.

Over in front of the bench Coach Wagon asked the ref, "Mr. Official, how come that wasn't a foul?"

"I didn't see a foul," he answered.

"Well I wonder if you might keep an eye on number 12 of their team," Coach Wagon continued. "He seems to be tackling our players while you're not watching."

The ref turned and glared at him. "Watch your mouth, coach," he said.

Coach Wagon then called over the other ref.

"All we're asking for is a fair chance," he said. "That guy isn't going to give it to us, but you can. Just try to be fair. That's all we want."

Ref number 2 looked at him and gave an almost imperceptible nod.

Back at the bench in the timeout, Coach Wagon eyed the team thoughtfully.

"All right, boys, you know what you're up against," he said. "Bullies and cheaters. It's up to you. Are you gonna give in or are you gonna fight back?"

It was Luke who answered. "I got this, coach."

Now we inbounded the ball to Luke with Limadeer guarding, crouched and ready to pounce. Luke dribbled the ball off to his right, tantalizing, and when Limadeer lunged for it, Luke calmly brought it behind his back, dribbled up court, sidestepped another defender, pulled up and shot an 18-foot jumper. Swish.

After the next Waterton basket, Limadeer again set up to full-court press Luke. This time Luke took a hard dribble and jab step to the right, then crossed over and went left right by the Rebel guard, who stumbled and tripped over his own feet. Limadeer recovered quickly and raced after Luke. But his head was down and so he didn't see that Luke had come to a dead stop, causing Limadeer to crash head first into Luke's back and fall to the ground.

Referee number 2 called a foul on the Waterton guard, and Luke casually dropped the ball on his head as he walked away. Limadeer looked like his head might explode. But he still thought he could get the best of this sophomore upstart.

So the next time Luke had the ball he backed off just a little, but was still pressing, ready to make the steal. This time Luke started left, then right, and Limadeer stayed right with him. Luke backed up a half-step, and when Limadeer advanced, Luke surged forward and dribbled the ball right through the defender's legs.

This time, however, he didn't pull up for a jump shot but continued driving to the basket and soared in for a slam dunk over Waterton's 6-foot-7 center. The Woodshed crowd was stunned into silence, but then a few gasps could be heard.

Waterton called timeout.

"Hey, Frank," Luke said as the teams walked to their benches. "Can you hear them? The crowd. They're laughing at you."

Now it was Limadeer's turn to bring the ball up court, and time to turn the tables as Luke now set up to full-court press him. Limadeer went right and then crossed over to go left, but Luke had anticipated the move and was standing there to take the charge. Referee number 2 signaled offensive foul.

"That's two fouls, Frank," Luke said. "Better take a seat."

But their coach left him in, and a minute later he had the ball in backcourt facing pressure from Luke again. This time he dribbled right, but when he reverse pivoted to go left, Luke snuck in behind him, swiped the ball cleanly, and headed in for a breakaway lay-up.

Limadeer would not be able to catch him and stop the basket, but as Luke soared in for a left-handed lay-up, he undercut him and knocked Luke's legs out from under him. It was the dirtiest play I think any of us had ever seen. Even the Woodshed crowd seemed dismayed, and you could hear some boos coming from them.

Luke could have been badly hurt, but whether it was due to luck or his incredible athletic ability, he managed to land on his side, protecting his head with his arms. After a few seconds he got up, shook his head and arms a little to reassure himself that he was all right, and walked casually to the free throw line.

This was Limadeer's third foul, and so he did go to the bench. Waterton had nobody who could stop Luke, and their coach was either too stubborn or not smart enough to either double-team him or switch to a zone defense. Luke poured in 28 points, and the rest of the team, realizing they didn't need to be intimidated, played as well as they had played all season. When the final buzzer sounded, we had won convincingly, 60-48, and Waterton's five-year home winning streak was history.

But bullies are often slow learners, and the longer they've been allowed to bully, the slower they learn.

Three weeks later Waterton came to our gym for a rematch. The place was packed, and I was super excited because for the first time I was suiting up for the varsity. I was having a pretty fair season on the junior varsity, and two of our varsity guys had gotten hurt, one in the last game and one in practice. Even though I was fairly certain I wouldn't get in the game, it was still a thrill to be wearing the varsity uniform and going through warm-ups in front of our home crowd.

And Luke, being the captain and my best friend, decided I should lead the team out onto the court. So when we heard the band strike up the first chords of Chicago's *25 Or 6 To 4,* we headed out to do our lay-ups. I tried to look cool and relaxed, like this was no big deal for me, but I think my heart rate was about 180. And when your heart rate is 180 it is pretty hard to shoot a lay-up. My first one almost broke the backboard and caromed out to about the free throw line. It was pretty embarrassing, and when I caught Luke's eye I could see him trying (unsuccessfully) to conceal a smirk. Fortunately, by the time the band was playing the next song, The Ventures' *Hawaii 5-0 Theme Song,* I had settled down and was doing the one thing I truly hoped for: blending in.

And then something happened that I'm pretty sure nobody had ever seen before or since. Waterton came out on the floor to warm up, but instead of going to their end of the court Frank Limadeer decided he would shadow Luke during our pre-game drills. So when Luke went up for a lay-up, Limadeer would jump up and block it. When someone would pass the ball to Luke, Limadeer would knock it away. And all the time he was talking trash to Luke.

For some hard-to-understand reason he still felt like he could intimidate this kid who was two years younger. It was like he had taken a page right out of Bruce Junkers' playbook. Luke just smiled and did his best to ignore the misguided pest.

But Coach Wagon did not want to just ignore it. "Hey coach," he said to Waterton's head man, a Mr. Mike Hoffee, "how about you tell your boy to get back on his side of the court."

"There's no rule against it," Coach Hoffee sneered back. "So how about you shut up and sit your Eskimo butt down on the bench."

Like I said: bullies ain't the sharpest knives in the drawer.

And while Luke chose to ignore Limadeer, I decided not to. So when he was getting up in Luke's face, I let loose a chest pass that ricocheted off the side of his face.

"Hey, watch it!" he shouted, turning his anger on me.

"Man, you need to work on your peripheral vision," I said. "You should have seen that coming."

But while he was seething at me, another errant pass hit him in the back of the head. Now he was really fit to be tied, and he turned and grabbed our closest teammate, Bill Sargent, who he figured had thrown the ball. Bill, probably our strongest and toughest player (not counting Luke, of course) was not about to back down and the two began to grapple.

Seeing this, the rest of the Waterton team was soon on our end of the court and it looked like a full-fledged melee was about to break out. But just then the referees emerged from the locker room and began to blow their whistles and rush into the middle of the scrum and break it up. When order was restored and both teams had returned to their benches, the head official called both coaches over to find out what had transpired.

Coach Wagon explained what Limadeer had done, and how Waterton's Coach Hoffee had refused to put a stop to it.

"There's no rule against it," Coach Hoffee explained again.

The official looked at him as if he was insane. Or psychotic. Which, I guess, he kind of was.

The head official was a highly respected prosecuting attorney in Tacoma who spent his days dealing with some of society's problem people, and a couple of nights a week he would referee high school basketball games. He had no patience for problem people infiltrating his nights. His name was Doug Wood, and oh, by the way, he had a brother named Frank Wood, who happened to have been our Woodlake Elementary School principal. That worked out pretty well for us.

Here's what he decided: two technical fouls against both Limadeer and Coach Hoffee, both ejected from the game; and one technical foul against each of the other 11 Waterton players and their assistant coach for going onto our end of the court to escalate the conflict. Altogether, 16 technical fouls against Waterton, which meant 32 free throws, before the game even started.

Luke went to the foul line as Limadeer and Coach Hoffee exited the gym, both fuming and spewing obscenities. The crowd cheered as Luke began to sink his free throws, and by the time he had made the first 15 it was about as loud as our home crowd had ever been. When he made his 25th in a row the noise was deafening. And when number 32 went in, which he shot left-handed by the way, I really thought my eardrums might burst.

So the game tipped off with the scoreboard reading Revere 32, Waterton 0. Needless to say we won easily: 94-40. Luke scored 52 (remember, this was before the 3-point shot was added), which is still a Hanahan County Conference record, while sitting out the last half of the third quarter and the whole fourth quarter.

(I actually got into the game late, although they had to remind me to take off my warm-up jacket when I checked in. I got the ball a couple of times and managed to not turn it over, although

I never once even entertained the thought of actually taking a shot.)

Teams either double-teamed Luke or played a box-and-one defense on him the rest of the season. We wound up with a 16-and-4 won-lost record, and didn't win the league championship.

But neither did Waterton. They lost twice to Brookfield and once to Balboa. Waterton's days of dominating through bullying and intimidation were over.

Thank you Luke Daisy.

Chapter 34

<u>Sweet Sixteen</u>

"Hang on to sixteen as long as you can. Changes come around real soon, make us women and men." – John Mellencamp

In January of our sophomore year we four guys – Luke, Johnny, Kenny, and I – all turned 16. Johnny and Kenny weren't allowed to get driver's licenses because of their disabilities, and Luke had very little interest in getting his. But I could hardly wait.

My birthday was on a Friday, so with school and basketball I would have to wait until Saturday to go take my test and get my coveted license. My concentration at school that day was not up to par, to say the least. At lunch I actually tried to take a bite of my *Twinkie* without remembering to take off the wrapper. And during the JV game that night my teammates, knowing it was my birthday, decided to feed me the ball so I could have an extra special game. I responded with a season-high 20. Only that wasn't my total of points, rebounds, or assists, but my combined total of missed shots and turnovers. Happy birthday to me.

But Saturday arrived and, sure enough, I passed the test and received my official Washington State Driver's License, number CATEEMK441TD. Kenny thought it was pretty cool that the license ended in TD.

"Yeah, for touchdown," I smiled.

"No, for total dork," he countered.

But a driver's license does you very little good without a car. My folks had started a savings account for me when I was born, mostly for college, and they had added to it every year. I also put a portion of my allowance, birthday, and Christmas money into it each year, and now they agreed to let me make a withdrawal to buy myself a car.

I had my eyes on a brand new, bright yellow, 1972 Dodge Charger, one of the great muscle cars of that era, sticker price $4,000. Not that I wanted to make a name for myself by having the fastest car in the school, but, you know, just in case someone pulled alongside at a light and challenged me I would be able to hold my own.

My parents, however, had a different idea. And so we called a family meeting to decide just what car I would be getting. I brought Luke along for support.

"Well, this is a family decision, so I think we should vote on whether you get a new or used car," my mom explained. I could see where this was going.

"Okay," I agreed, "but you have to let me make my case for the Charger. And, I think Luke should get to vote, too. You've always said he's like family, and this does kind of concern him as well."

Mom and dad looked at each other and then nodded. "Okay. Go ahead, Michael," dad said.

"As you know," I began making my case, "I have maintained a perfect 4.0 Grade Point Average, and done all my chores faithfully without complaining. I think that kind of responsibility should be rewarded. Also, I will often be driving with extremely valuable cargo on board, namely Luke, Johnny, Kenny, and Ellie. I think we owe it to them and their families to provide the safest, most dependable means of transportation, which is clearly a new car."

My parents nodded. "Is that it?" dad asked.

"Yes."

"Okay then. Michael you have made a very nice case," mom said. "Now it's time to vote. All in favor of Michael getting a dependable used car, raise your hand." Mom and dad both raised their hands.

"All in favor of Michael getting a brand new Dodge Charger raise your hand," she continued.

My hand shot up, but I looked over at Luke and he didn't follow suit.

"Hey, why aren't you raising your hand?" I asked.

"I'm abstaining," he said.

"What?!"

"Your mom's about to feed me dinner," he explained. "I'm not going to vote against her."

"Well, thanks a lot pal."

I was defeated and dejected.

"One more vote," dad continued. "Everybody who thinks Michael should be extremely grateful that he is going to get a car, any car, raise your hand."

All 3 of them raised a hand, and then, reluctantly, I made it unanimous.

"Well I guess that's settled then," mom said. "I thought that went well, don't you Michael?"

I just gave her my best pouty face.

"Wait," Luke interjected. "Everybody who thinks the wonderful, generous, kind - and might I add good-looking - Cateere family should also buy Luke a car, raise your hand." Luke's hand went up.

"All opposed?" I added quickly, giving Luke the evil eye. This time my hand shot up, joining my parents.

He shrugged. "Oh well. It was worth a shot."

And so it was decided that my first car would not be a shiny-yellow, brand-new, super-fast Dodge Charger muscle car, but a used, four-door, never-win-a-race, four-year-old, Oldsmobile Vista Cruiser, with 30,000 miles and a $1,000 price tag. I was sure the only reason it didn't have more miles on it was that the owners had probably been 100 years old and could no longer drive. It had a dark brown exterior with a light brown roof, and a brown vinyl interior with bench seats. I'm not really sure of the engine size, but I think it was about 18 horse power. If you looked up "dull" in the dictionary, you would have seen a picture of my 1968 Vista Cruiser. I named it Victor, although Kenny was quick to point out that if you're going to name a car you should name it Otto. I kind of hated it — at least I acted like I did - and could hardly wait for it to break down so I could upgrade. Wouldn't you know it? That car, with some help from Matthew Daisy and his fantastic automotive skills, lasted 18 years and over 250,000 miles.

It was the best car I ever had.

Spring rolled around and it was time for baseball season. The good news was that we were going to have a very good team, with several players from our Little League World Series squad. The bad news was that Paul Revere's much-loved, highly successful coach, Harry Orr, had just turned 65 and decided to retire so that he could spend more time with his grandchildren.

And the even worse news was that the Bonney Flats School District, in its infinite wisdom, had decided to hire Coach Jeego as our head coach.

Coach Jeego's unexplainable grudge against Luke seemed to have intensified after Luke's tremendous success in basketball, as more and more people openly questioned his weird decision to not allow Luke to play varsity football.

Luke just went about his business and, of course, was a shining star during tryouts. After 3 days of practice Coach Jeego posted the results on the locker room bulletin board. On the first page were the names of the 12 boys who had made the varsity. Luke's name was not on it.

On the second page was the list of 11 boys who had been selected for the junior varsity. My name was listed, but Luke's was not. But at the bottom of the page, in small lettering, was the word "over." And there on the back of that page was one name: Luke Daisy. Coach Jeego had not only taken his best player and assigned him to the JV squad, but had done his best to humiliate Luke by making it look like he was an afterthought.

All of the players were angry, but nobody dared say anything to our tyrant of a coach. Our JV coach Mr. Max Patrick, however, resigned in protest. Even though he would have benefitted from having Luke on his team, and probably could have used the extra coaching money, he could not bring himself to work for someone so petty. It was a pretty good lesson for us in integrity.

Still, I felt like I had to do something, so I went to talk to Luke's dad.

"Mr. Daisy," I said. "I know you hate to run interference for us, but this is so wrong. You have to go to the school and do something about it. It's just not fair to Luke."

"You're right, it's not fair," he said. "But I don't think there's anything I can do. I'm pretty sure talking to Coach Jeego won't do any good."

I had come prepared.

"It says in Nehemiah 4 that we should fight for our families," I pleaded. "And Isaiah 61 says the Lord loves justice. And in Amos 5 it says to let justice roll on like a mighty river. I think that all means we have to do something."

Mr. Daisy nodded and smiled.

"Michael, I'm glad to see you using Bible verses to make a point," he said. "Just be sure that you look to the Word to see God's leading, and not to cherry-pick verses that will support what you've already decided.

"I just don't think this is a battle that I'm being called to fight. I'm sorry."

It may have been the only time that I was unhappy and disagreed with Mr. Daisy. So then I went and tried to make my case to my dad.

"I will go talk to him, Michael," he said, "but I think Mr. Daisy is right, it won't do any good."

"What I don't understand is why Coach Jeego has it in for Luke," I said.

"Well, there's something you have to understand," dad explained. "Coach Jeego's wife, Betsy, is Mr. Junkers sister."

"You mean Coach Jeego is Bruce Junkers' uncle?"

"That's right."

"But dad, how come the Junkers have so much animosity for the Daisy family?"

"Well, that goes back a long time, before you were even born. You see, Jack Junkers used to be an elder in our church. But when he inherited all his money and became filthy rich, he changed. He had an affair with his secretary and left his wife, then hired a high-priced attorney to take Bruce away from her and gain full custody.

"Pastor Daisy confronted him and told him that he would have to step down as an elder. Mr. Junkers was furious and thought Pastor Daisy was trying to humiliate him. He said he would leave the church and take all of his money with him. Pastor Daisy told him that God didn't want his money, He wanted his heart. So Mr. Junkers left and threatened to get even. That's what he's been trying to do ever since."

"Wow," I said. "I had no idea. I guess that helps explain a lot."

"Still, I'll go and talk to coach Jeego," dad agreed. "I guess it couldn't hurt."

And so dad headed to school and into the coaches' room to see if he could talk some sense into Coach Jeego. As the school's team doctor he had access to all of the facilities.

Coach Jeego looked up at him suspiciously when he entered the room.

"What do you want, doc?" he said.

"Hugh, I came to talk to you about Luke Daisy," dad explained.

"There's nothing to talk about," the coach responded. "End of discussion."

"Hugh, half the town is angry with you, and the other half thinks you're crazy," dad continued. "Is that what you want?"

"Now you listen to me," the coach yelled, red-faced and rising to get up and point a finger at dad's chest.

But he never finished his point. Instead he tried to get a breath, broke out in a sweat, grabbed his chest and fell back in his chair. Dad recognized immediately what was happening: heart attack. He started CPR and got one of the other coaches to call an ambulance, which took the coach to the hospital.

It turned out to be a mild myocardial infarction, and he would have a full recovery, thanks in large part to dad's quick actions. Coach Jeego had some arthrosclerosis (hardening of the arteries) that he would need to be treated for, but eventually he would be fine.

The "eventually" part meant that his doctors told him he would not be coaching baseball that spring.

With our first game fast-approaching, the school board reached out to Coach Orr to see if he would consider coming out of retirement to take the reins of this year's team. He readily agreed, and Paul Revere High School baseball was back in good hands.

But not before Coach Jeego made one final attempt to influence things.

"Listen, Harry," he said to Coach Orr, who was visiting him in the hospital. "Don't forget this is my team. You are just an interim coach. Don't be making any changes to my roster."

Coach Orr smiled and patted him on the shoulder.

"Hugh, you just worry about getting better," he said, getting up to leave. "But make no mistake. This is my team now."

Of course that meant his first order of business was moving Luke up to the Varsity where he belonged, as the starting shortstop and leadoff hitter, where he ended up leading the league in batting and stolen bases. Led by Luke and our former Little League stars William Botts, Mike Monroe, and Gary Radliffe, along with Coach Orr's great leadership, Paul Revere High School cruised to the 1972 state baseball championship.

It was Luke's first high school state championship. It wouldn't be his last.

Chapter 35

The Power of Music

"Where words fail, music speaks." – Hans Christian Andersen

Isn't it funny how music can instantly transport you to a specific time and place in your life and trigger powerful emotions? When you hear a certain song you find yourself travelling back in your mind to when you first heard it, or to where you most remember listening to it. Whenever I hear *Yellow Submarine* (Beatles), *Wild Thing* (Troggs), *Summer in the City* (Lovin' Spoonful), or *Cherish* (The Association), I'm right back in my bedroom fighting meningitis in the fall of 1966.

And there are several songs in my life that carry me right back to the spring and summer of 1972.

At the end of every school year, Paul Revere would put on an all-school talent show. The gym would be packed with parents and students for a three-hour, Friday night production of acts - mostly musical, but also magic and comedy – from its students and faculty. It was called *The Spectacular*, and even though many of the performances were far less than spectacular, it was truly one of the highlights of the year.

That year Kenny was chosen to be the host, even though he was only a sophomore. He was easily the most talented kid in the school, and the obvious choice to lead the show. And he absolutely killed it.

By that time he had been in a wheelchair for three months, and his pancreas had begun to shut down so that he was now insulin dependent. But nothing seemed to dampen his enthusiasm, or curb his sense of humor, or limit his drive to keep improving as an entertainer. He continued to amaze us with his courage and attitude. "I'm just not afraid," he said. "I know this is the life God has chosen for me, so it must be okay." He had *"Jeremiah 29:11"* written on the side of all his shoes: *"For I know the plans I have for you, declares the Lord … plans to give you hope and a future."*

"I'm going to hold onto that as long as I can," he would say.

Kenny started the night out by wheeling out onto the stage and welcoming everybody, and then apologizing for not standing up during the national anthem. "Lately I've found it easier to sing sitting down," he deadpanned.

Soon he had the whole audience singing the theme song to *Gilligan's Island* *("Just sit right back and you'll hear a tale …")* and *The Beverly Hillbillies* *("Come and listen to a story about a man named Jed …")*

"All right now, everybody together," he continued. "The Declaration of Independence: 'When in the course of human events ….'" He stopped and turned the microphone to the audience. Silence, and then laughter.

"Let's try again," he went on. "The Preamble to the Constitution: 'We the people of these United States …'" Again he stopped and aimed the mic at the crowd. No words from the audience, just a lot more laughter.

Kenny then looked down and shook his head in feigned sadness. "Does this concern anyone else?" he asked. "We know more about the Clampetts and the castaways than our country's history. I guess our founding fathers really messed up by not coming up with a catchy theme song."

The whole night was a huge hit. Millie Morgan belted out a medley of Carole King songs from the *Tapestry* album that brought a standing ovation. Karen Paulsen sat on Kenny's lap and they sang a duet of Sonny & Cher's *"I've Got You Babe"* that had everyone cheering wildly. But when they finished she suggested they sing *"These Boots Are Made For Walking"* and Kenny just slumped his shoulders, shook his head and got that real disappointed look on his face again. "Really?" he said. The crowd ate it up, knowing of course that Kenny himself had written all the jokes.

One of the highlights of the night, though, was Johnny and Luke doing Abbott & Costello's *"Who's on First?"* routine. Johnny had rolled on the floor laughing when he'd seen it on TV, had convinced his mom to take him to the library so he could get a copy of it, and had memorized the whole thing. Then he talked Luke into doing it with him for the show, and to keep it a secret from everybody. Only Johnny would have been able to get Luke voluntarily that far out of his comfort zone.

So we were all shocked when the two most mismatched twins in history walked out on stage, Luke in a baggy old baseball uniform and Johnny wearing a wool suit and bow tie. Halfway through the hilarious routine Luke forgot his next line, and Johnny leaned over and whispered it to him. The crowd, already in stitches, roared, especially when Johnny shook his head, rolled his eyes, and pointed his thumb at his brother as if to say, "Can you believe this guy?!"

After three hours Kenny rolled back out to the middle of the stage and announced, "I'm sure you're all ready to go home. So let's finish with a song about someone else who's ready to go home."

Then a group of guys from the choir dressed in white bell-bottoms (called swabbies) and surfer shirts, carrying a surfboard, walked out on stage as a band struck up the first note of the Beach Boys' *"Sloop John B."*

"We come on the Sloop John B," Kenny sang.

"My grandfather and me. Around Nassau town we did roam."

The crowd was standing and singing along by the time he got to the chorus for the first time.

"So, hoist up the John B sails. See how the main sail sets."

The harmonies were perfect and Kenny sounded like he was channeling Brian Wilson.

"Let me go home. Why don't they let me go home? Well, I feel so broke up. I wanna go home."

If you closed your eyes you might have thought you were actually at a Beach Boys concert.

"Sherriff John Stone. Why don't you leave me alone? I feel so broke up. I wanna go home."

And then the final verse:

"The poor cook he caught the fits. And threw away all my grits. Then he took and he ate up all of my corn. Let me go home. Why don't they let me go home?"

Then suddenly the music came to an abrupt stop. All of us in the audience who had been loudly singing along drew quickly quiet, wondering what had happened. And then the spotlight shone directly on Kenny.

Who put his hands on the side of his wheelchair, and slowly, ever so slowly, pushed himself up and onto his feet. Where he delivered perfectly the next line of the great song from a standing position.

"This is the worst trip, I've ever been on."

The crowd … went … wild!!! Like nothing I had ever heard or seen. Mouths gaped open, tears streamed, and a gymnasium full of people screamed so loud that nobody could hear the final chorus. Despite what the song said, I don't think anybody was thinking "I wanna go home."

All these years later, I know there are about 3,000 people who will never hear *Sloop John B* without thinking of our amazing friend, Ken Carew.

A couple of weeks later, shortly after the school year ended, Luke and I dropped Ellie off at Lincoln Lake, where she was working as a lifeguard for the summer, and headed to Bluto's to meet up with Johnny and Kenny.

"You want a soda?" Luke asked as we walked in.

"Sure, thanks. It's on me," I said, handing him a dollar. "I'll go find Kenny and Johnny."

So Luke went to the front counter to get us a couple of Cokes while I walked around the back to where the tables were. I found Kenny and Johnny sitting, along with another one of our friends, Mark Brewster, and Johnny's friend Ryan.

But they weren't alone.

Bruce Junkers and his sidekick Marv Snortberry were standing over them, eating their french fries and taunting them.

"What's going on?" I said walking up to the table, looking at Bruce. I had never once been in a fight, but I had a sinking feeling that this might be my first one, and I just might be in for a beating.

"This doesn't concern you, Cateere," he sneered. "We're just sharing their french fries."

"I believe the word you're looking for is stealing, not sharing," Kenny responded, smiling.

Bruce started to answer, but stopped talking and backed up a step when he looked up and saw Luke walking around the corner towards us. Luke didn't say a word but walked directly at Bruce, and when he was a few steps away tripped over his own feet and both sodas flew out of his hands and all over Bruce and Marv. It was the only time I ever saw Luke "accidentally" trip. It looked so real, I think maybe he had learned it from Kenny.

Bruce's face turned red and he spat out, "You rotten punk," and took a wild swing at Luke. Luke ducked and delivered a full-force right hand that caught the bully right in the midsection. Junkers doubled over and hit the floor, the wind completely knocked out of him.

Marv took a moment to absorb the whole scene, and then turned to leave. But I was feeling kind of brave, so I grabbed him by the arm. "Not so fast, Snortberry," I said. "You owe these guys for the food you stole. I think a couple of bucks should do it."

Marv hesitated, but then looked at Luke, down at Bruce, and reached into his pocket and dropped a couple of one dollar bills on the table. Again he turned to leave, but this time Kenny stopped him.

"Hey Marv," he said.

"What?" Marv asked, turning back around.

"You know there are two paths you can go by. But in the long run, there's still time to change the road you're on."

Marv just scoffed and walked off. Bruce got his breath back shortly thereafter and followed him out the door, still hunched over.

"I'll go get some towels and clean up this mess," Luke said, but then turned to Kenny. "That was pretty profound about the two paths, Hoppy," he said. "Where did you get that? Is it from a Bible verse?"

"Nope," Kenny answered. "Led Zeppelin. *Stairway to Heaven.*"

(In an interesting sidelight, Marv Snortberry did eventually change the road he was on. Years later a drug problem cost him his job and his marriage, and he hit rock bottom. Ironically, it was Matthew Daisy who reached out and helped him turn his life around, giving him a job, a place to live, and paying for his rehab. Marv then became a volunteer at the Bonney Flats Juvenile Detention Center, where I heard he made a big difference in the lives of a lot of troubled youth. You just never know.)

Chapter 36

The Music Dies

"Something touched me deep inside. The day the music died." –
Don McLean

On February 3, 1959 pilot Roger Peterson took off in his Beechcraft Bonanza from the Mason City, Iowa airport, headed up to Fargo, North Dakota. The weather was abysmal, and the inexperienced pilot had no business trying to fly in it. Five miles north of the airport the plane crashed, killing the pilot and his three passengers.

Those passengers were 22-year-old Buddy Holly, the king of rock & roll; 17-year-old Ritchie Valens, who had set the music world ablaze with his hit song *La Bamba*; and 28-year-old J.P. Richardson, also known as The Big Bopper, of *Chantilly Lace* fame.

In New York, 13-year-old Don McLean, a huge Buddy Holly fan, read about the crash the following morning while folding newspapers for his paper route. Twelve years later the singer-songwriter memorialized the crash as "the day the music died" in his mega-hit song *American Pie*.

For us, the day the music died was Thursday, July 20, 1972. It was the fourth anniversary of that first Special Olympics, and the third anniversary of that first moon landing.

Johnny died.

It happened quickly. He got a bad cold, which turned into pneumonia, and a week later he was gone. Like so many with

Down syndrome, he had been born with a congenital heart defect (CHD) which led to circulatory and respiratory issues. Eventually his heart – the biggest heart any of us ever knew – stopped being able to pump enough blood and oxygen through his weak body.

I was in my room reading Richard Adams' wonderful new book *Watership Down* when dad came in and told me we needed to get to the hospital because Johnny wasn't doing well. He lay on his back, eyes closed, and took his last breath surrounded by all the people who loved him most. Luke had climbed up onto the bed with him, his brother's head resting on his powerful chest. Johnny had come into this world holding Luke's hand, and 16 years later he left the same way.

When the nurse came and told us it was time to leave so they could take Johnny's body, Luke refused to move. He just lay there sobbing, holding his brother, willing him back to life. He wouldn't listen to his mom or dad or brothers.

Finally, for some reason, it was Ellie who got through to him.

"Lukie," she spoke gently, caressing his forehead. "Johnny Bear is gone. This isn't him anymore. He flew away. This is just his very tired, less-than-perfect body. I think he's already got a new body and can run faster than any of us. Maybe even on the moon, like he said."

Luke nodded slowly, and we all walked out of the room together. All smaller. All changed forever. A part of each of us had died along with the boy with the damaged brain and the golden heart.

We never heard Mrs. Daisy sing again.

Johnny's memorial service was held a week later at the high school gym because Bonney Flats Baptist Church wouldn't have been large enough to hold everybody. Indeed, there were about 2,000 people there.

Matthew and Mark Daisy conducted the service, and they did a wonderful job. Luke still hadn't said a word since Johnny passed. Mark, without a doubt the smartest person in the building, talked about how he had learned a lot more from his brother than his brother had learned from him, and how all the learning in the world did you no good if you weren't able to love and be loved.

"The wizard tells the tin man that a heart is measured not by how much you love, but by how much you are loved," he said. "But I think he was wrong. He was a fake, after all. Because I think a heart is measured by both. And the truth is: nobody I know loved others more than Johnny Daisy, and nobody was loved more than Johnny Daisy.

Matthew brought in some of the drawings that Johnny had sent him when he was in Vietnam. Almost every day Johnny had drawn a picture with his crayons – usually a stick figure of a boy with an animal - and sent it to Matthew, and at the bottom of every page he had scrawled in big letters I Love You. Of course the L was backwards and the words were slanted and ran together. Matthew had saved every one.

"I'm certainly no art expert," he said at the service, "but I can tell you that these are more valuable to me than all the Rembrandt's and da Vinci's in the world."

Many people told stories about Johnny and the amazing way that all of the animals loved him. Mr. & Mrs. Hosserous told the story of how Johnny had befriended Ryan and gave him a reason to smile every day. Ellie talked about the joy everyone felt when Johnny had been chosen king of the ninth grade dance. Several people mentioned his gold medal that he wore around his neck every day for the last four years.

Kenny sang Johnny's two favorite songs, *"Jesus Loves Me"* and *"You Are My Sunshine,"* that Mrs. Daisy had sung to him when she tucked him in every night. Only he couldn't make it through *"You are My Sunshine"*, but choked up halfway through.

Wouldn't you know it was Luke, who couldn't sing a lick, who got up and helped Kenny finish.

"You make me happy when skies are gray. You'll never know, dear, how much I love you. Please don't take my sunshine away."

It's funny how courage can show up when and where you might least expect it.

But Luke was still inconsolable.

"Don't you see?" he tried to explain. "It's my fault Johnny had his difficulties. We were in the womb together and I stole from him. We were supposed to share everything, but I took all the good stuff. It just wasn't fair."

"That's crazy, Luke," I said. "You can't blame yourself. Johnny loved you more than anyone else in the whole world."

Dad tried to explain that that's not how it works in the womb. And Mr. Daisy said, "Son, God didn't make a mistake with Johnny, or with you, or with any of us. Just like it says in Psalms,

He created our innermost being and knit us together in our mother's womb."

"I know, dad," Luke answered. "And I want to believe all of the things people are saying about how he's in a better place and everything is perfect for him now. But it's hard, because I'm so sad. I just wish maybe God would give me a sign or something to let me know that it's all right. I keep praying for a sign. Is that wrong?"

"No, son, I don't think that's wrong," Mr. Daisy said. "We all struggle with doubt at times. Your mother and I are struggling with this, too. I'm guessing we always will. And who knows? Maybe God will give you some kind of a sign."

A week later Kenny and I convinced Luke to go to Lincoln Lake with us.

"I don't feel like swimming," Luke said.

"And I certainly don't," responded Kenny, who was now in his wheelchair about half the time. Some days he could stand and walk, but other days he didn't have the strength or the balance.

"I don't feel like going in the water either," I added. "We'll just go and sit in the grass, visit with Ellie when she's on a break, and talk about Johnny. Remember how much he loved the lake? I think it will do us good."

And so we went, and it was good. We cried a little and we laughed a little. Just what we needed.

And then it happened. I was the first to look up and see them approaching. It took me a moment to really grasp what I was seeing, but when I did I let out a little gasp. Luke and Kenny looked at me, and then turned to see what I was seeing.

There were probably two dozen of them heading our way, walking slowly but with a definite purpose. They didn't stop until they had completely surrounded Luke, some crawling up on his lap, others resting all around him.

Ducks.

The same ducks that Johnny used to feed. We had no food, but they didn't seem to care. They weren't there to be fed, they were there to give comfort. And, who knows, maybe to receive some as well.

Luke, tears now pouring down his cheeks, looked up at the sky, lifted his hands and said, "Thank you."

It's funny how God can show up when and how you might least expect it.

I know that everyone is entitled to their own opinions, and there are those who think if an amniocentesis test shows the presence of Down syndrome in an unborn baby you'd be doing the family and the world in general a favor by ending that pregnancy. Just don't try to convince the people of Bonney Flats, Washington – those who loved and were loved by Johnny Daisy, whose lives were made so much richer for knowing him. Unless of course you're fond of tar and feathers.

Chapter 37

Junior Year

"Adversity causes some men to break; others to break records."
– William Arthur Ward

In late August we began two-a-day football practices as we prepared for our junior season. Coach Jeego had returned, fully recovered, and meaner than ever. I think Kenny may have had the best description of him: "His bite is worse than his bark, but not as bad as his breath."

And the coach had a new plan to prevent Luke from playing quarterback. For the first time in his coaching career he decided he would use a full platoon system, meaning players could only play offense or defense. Luke would be a defensive player, while Jerry Hadrick, a senior who just happened to be Coach Jeego's nephew, would play quarterback. Jerry was a decent guy, and it certainly wasn't his fault that he got picked to run the team over Luke. He ended up taking a lot of unfair abuse, although nobody was a bigger supporter of his than Luke.

I was chosen to be a first-team wide receiver. It was an honor that I felt really good about, except that being a wide receiver in Coach Jeego's offense was kind of like being a sprig of parsley on the plate of a beautiful prime rib dinner: you didn't really do anything, but were just there for show.

In those days most high schools played a traditional 5-2-4 defense – five down linemen, two linebackers, and four defensive backs. Coach Wagon, our defensive coordinator, designed a special defense with Luke in mind, a 5-2-3-1: five down linemen, two linebackers, three defensive backs, and

Luke. Officially his position was called a Rover, but it meant that he could use his uncanny anticipation and athletic skills to line up wherever he wanted and do whatever he thought was best on any given play. If the other team had a star receiver, Luke could line up and cover him. If they had an outstanding running back, Luke could line up at middle linebacker and shadow him wherever he went. Sometimes he lined up as a deep safety, other times he would come up to the line and rush the quarterback off the edge. The other teams would pretty much just have to guess where he would be and try to handle him. Mostly, they were unsuccessful.

A week before the season started Luke and I went in to see our wonderful principal, Mr. Eilertson, to tell him an idea I had. To honor Johnny, I wanted to know if the two of us could sew a "JBD" patch on the shoulders of our uniforms (John Barnabas Daisy).

Mr. Eilertson listened, but then shook his head. "I'm sorry boys. League rules specify that all of the uniforms, with the exception of the jersey numbers, have to be identical."

We nodded, thanked him anyway, and turned to leave.

"So," he said before we reached the door, "I guess that means we'll have to sew a 'JBD' patch on the shoulders of *every* uniform. I think it's a great idea."

We were overjoyed, as were the rest of our teammates. Not so much Coach Jeego. When he saw what had been done he marched into Mr. Eilertson's office.

"Just whose idea was this whole patch thing, Tom?" he demanded.

"It was my idea, Hugh," Mr. Eilertson answered. "And I think it's a very good one."

"Well, I'm the head football coach. Why wasn't I consulted on this?"

"Because, Hugh, I knew you would be against it. And frankly, I don't really care what you think about it." Clearly Mr. Eilertson was one of a large group of people who had had it up to here with this man.

Coach Jeego just glared.

"Don't forget, Hugh: you report to me. It's true that you are the head football coach, but only as long as I allow you to be," Mr. Eilertson continued. "You understand that, right?"

Coach Jeego didn't answer.

"One more thing, coach. I've been watching your practices and I see that you've decided not to play Luke Daisy on offense. Why is that?"

"I just think we'll be better off if we play different kids on offense and defense."

"First time for that, huh?"

"That's right."

"It's like you've got Superman on your team, but you'd rather he spend the whole time as Clark Kent."

The two just stared at each other for a moment, until Coach Jeego asked, "Is that all?"

"Yes, Hugh, that's all. You can go now."

When Coach Wagon heard about the conversation he changed the name of Luke's position from Rover to Superman.

That fall we won 7 games and lost 2 (because we "just weren't tough enough"). In the 9 games I caught a total of 9 passes, thank you very much. The good news was that I didn't drop any.

Luke, on the other hand, had an unbelievable year. (I guess I really shouldn't use the word "unbelievable" to describe anything Luke did.) He had 12 interceptions, which was the most in the state. He led our team in tackles and quarterback sacks. And even though he didn't play a single down on offense, he still scored 13 touchdowns: 4 each on kick returns, punt returns, and interception returns, and one more on a fumble return. He was named First Team All-State defensive back and special teams player, the first Revere High School player to be named all state since John Pearson, a tackle on the 1969 team.

I had this vision of every coach in the league getting together after the season and sending Coach Jeego a giant thank you card for NOT letting Luke play offense. Every time I walked past his office I looked to see if there might be a beautiful floral arrangement on his desk. I never saw one, but then maybe he had just dumped it in the trash.

Basketball season our junior year produced something I never thought I'd see: a team with Luke on it losing almost as much as it won. We won 12 games and lost 8, which was probably close to the total number of games Luke had lost in his entire life.

The problem, of course, wasn't Luke. He was the best player in the league, maybe even the state. The problem was the rest of us. We were a team full of juniors, and with the exception of the few minutes I had logged the year before, we had no varsity experience. So every game Luke would get double-teamed, and the rest of us would do our best to score, which shouldn't have been that hard since it was 4 against 3. One of the local writers referred to us as "Luke and the Pips," and said that just like the man in Gladys Knight's great song *Midnight Train to Georgia*, Luke was "a superstar that wouldn't get far" this season. It was pretty clever, but not very nice.

Luke managed to average 20 points a game, many of them on lay-ins after steals before the other team could set up their double-team, and many of them on free throws when the only way the other team could stop him was to foul him. Coach Wagon kept trying to get him to shoot more, but Luke couldn't help himself from passing to the open man. It's just that the open man — often me — had trouble putting the ball in the basket.

Coach Wagon was always encouraging us, telling us that if we just kept working hard, our time would come. And we did get better. In fact, we won our last four games so that we finished with a winning record. Two of our wins that year came against Waterton, and two were against our cross-town rival Madison, so the season wasn't a total loss.

Luke was selected First Team All-State, the only athlete in all of Washington to be given that honor for both football and basketball. His legend just kept on growing.

And that legend grew by leaps and bounds in the springtime.

On the second day of baseball practice, Luke was standing just outside the dugout getting ready to take batting practice when another player, not paying attention, took a practice swing and clobbered Luke's left forearm. The sound of that aluminum bat connecting with Luke's arm was so loud, everybody stopped to see what had happened just as Luke collapsed to the ground in agony.

The x-rays showed a clean break of the ulna. He would spend the next 3 months in a cast, and there would be no baseball season for Luke in 1973.

But that didn't mean there would be no sports.

"Hey, just because I can't swing a bat doesn't mean I can't run or jump," Luke said, explaining that he would now be a member of the track team. "This stupid cast ain't on my leg."

We had a pretty good track team already, partly because a lot of the school's best athletes opted to avoid baseball with coach Jeego, and partly because the track coaches were the extremely well-liked Mr. Gallo and Mrs. Preciado. He coached the running events and she coached the field events. Although sad about Luke's broken arm, both coaches were thrilled to have him as part of the team.

Luke decided to compete in the 880-yard run (remember, this was before the commies convinced us to switch to metric) and the Triple Jump, and he also wound up running in the 440-yard relay and mile relay. He was already in great shape from football and basketball, but running a half-mile required a new kind of fitness. And while he had incredible springs in his legs, he had to learn the right techniques to master the triple jump. To nobody's surprise, Luke was up to both tasks.

After a few days of track practice Luke was walking back up to the locker room, and I joined him as baseball practice had just ended as well. But then he said, "Come on, Mouse," and we veered off to the tennis courts to watch the end of their practice. One of our friends, Burke Lee, was a star on the tennis team, and had actually finished fourth in state as a junior the year before.

Their practice was just ending, and Burke was the last one out there, practicing his serve.

"Can I volley with you, Burke?" Luke asked.

"Sure. Come on in," he answered.

So Luke grabbed one of Burke's extra rackets and the two started hitting back and forth. Luke had never played competitively, or had any lessons, but we played a lot during the summer for fun, often just to work up a good sweat before heading to Lincoln Lake. And tennis was a perfect sport for Luke, with his quickness, power, and natural hand-eye coordination. Before long Burke was hitting hard ground strokes at Luke, and Luke was returning almost all of them. After about 15 minutes they called it quits.

"Man, you should have joined tennis instead of track," Burke said.

"Thanks," Luke answered. "That would have been fun. But I don't really know how to serve well, or hit a backhand." When we played tennis in the summer Luke wouldn't hit a backhand but would just switch the racket to his left hand, since he was about as close to ambidextrous as you can get. He couldn't do that now with his left arm in a cast.

"Well, I could have taught you those things," Burke said.

As we headed into the locker room, a crazy thought occurred to me.

"Hey, I wonder if they would allow you to play both sports," I said. "The tennis matches are on Tuesdays and Thursdays, and the track meets are on Fridays."

Luke stopped walking and turned to stare at me, pondering what I had just suggested. Then we hustled into the locker room to check with the coaches to see what they thought of the idea, not to mention if it was even allowed under our league and state rules. Neither Mr. Gallo nor Mrs. Preciado, or the tennis coach Mr. Madden, knew the answer about if it was explicitly prohibited, so we'd have to check with the principal, Mr. Eilertson. But all three coaches were eager to find out, and all three were fully supportive of the idea.

Mr. Eilertson checked all of the league handbooks and made a few phone calls to representatives of the Washington Interscholastic Athletic Association. Nobody had ever heard of it happening, but nobody could find a reason why it couldn't be done, so Luke got the go-ahead. "You'll need a special parental consent form that I'll put together," Mr. Eilertson explained, "and the coaches will have to accommodate you to meet the minimum requirements for practices attended in order to compete in both sports."

And so Luke's *two-sports-in-one-season* experiment began. On Monday's he would spend an hour at track practice and then an hour at tennis. Tuesdays and Thursdays were tennis matches. Wednesday he would start with an hour of tennis practice, and then head to the track. Fridays were the track meets. And Saturdays, Luke and Burke would head to the Bonney Flats Tennis Club, where Burke's family had a membership, and they would play for hours. Sometimes they would play singles against each other, and sometimes they would play doubles against some of the club's best older players.

Luke started out playing number 3 singles, but after wiping out all of his opponents he was moved up to number 2 singles, where he continued to win all of his matches. As the regular season wound down, he and Burke were pretty much evenly matched.

In track Luke barely won his first couple of 880-yard races, but as the season went on his margins of victory got bigger and bigger and his winning times got faster and faster. He also won every Triple Jump competition, and at the last regular season meet jumped 48 feet, which was the highest mark in the state that year.

Both Luke and Burke qualified for the state tennis tournament, which would be held in Spokane on Wednesday and Thursday, May 23 and 24. And Luke qualified for state track in the 880-yard run and the Triple Jump, along with the mile relay. That meet was scheduled for Friday and Saturday, May 25 and 26, in Seattle, the complete opposite end of the state.

It was going to be a week that nobody would soon forget.

Our baseball season was over (all you need to know about how I did is that my batting average was less than my weight, and I tipped the scales at about 175 pounds), and Mom and dad had let me take the time off school to travel with Luke, Burke, and Mr. Madden to Spokane for the tennis finals. Luke and Burke each won their first two singles matches in straight sets on Wednesday, and Luke survived a tough semifinal match on Thursday, 6-4, 4-6, 6-4. But Burke lost in the other semifinals, 6-4, 7-5, to the same boy who had won the state championship each of the past two years. Luke and Burke then combined for an easy win in the doubles finals Thursday morning, 6-1, 6-1.

If you were to draw a caricature of a condescending snob, it would probably look a lot like J.A. Walker, Luke's opponent in the singles finals Thursday evening. He had played tennis from the time he was old enough for the family butler to put a racket in his hand, and he had not lost a match in three years of high school varsity competition. This would be his third straight state championship after he disposed of Luke. The idea of having to play a boy who wasn't even the number 1 player on his team, who had just started playing competitively this year, and who frankly looked like he belonged on a football field more than a tennis court – well, it almost seemed insulting to Walker. He didn't bother to shake Luke's hand when they headed onto the court for the start of the championship match.

Luke just smiled and shook his head.

The first set Luke hit nothing but drop shots and lob shots, making his opponent charge up to the net and then sprint back to the baseline. Even when Luke had what looked like a sure winner he would hit it soft enough that Walker could sprint and get to the ball. It almost looked like he wasn't trying hard enough to win the points, and sure enough the first set ended with Luke losing, 6-0.

But any questions I might have had about Luke's strategy ended quickly when I saw Walker between sets. He was exhausted. Luke had totally worn him out. Now Luke was bouncing around, ready to start the second set, while Walker stayed in his chair breathing heavily until the tournament official told him he had to get back out on the court.

And then it was like a tiger pouncing on his helpless prey. Luke was flying all over the court, while Walker looked like his legs were made of putty and his feet were made of concrete. After winning the second and third sets, 6-0, 6-0, Luke Daisy was the 1973 Class AAA State tennis champion. And along with Burke's third place finish in singles, and the two of them winning the doubles crown, Paul Revere High School had easily won another team state championship to go along with last year's baseball title.

Now it was time for the five-hour drive back across the mountains because the state track meet was set to start the following morning. Unfortunately, as we neared Snoqualmie Pass a major accident had caused a semi-trailer to jackknife across both lanes of I-90 westbound, forcing the road to close completely. Luke had to sleep in the back seat of Mr. Madden's station wagon while we waited four hours for a wrecker to come up from Yakima and get the road cleared.

We used a pay phone in North Bend to let our folks know what was going on, and we didn't get back to Bonney Flats until 8 a.m. Mrs. Daisy met us at the school with Luke's track uniform, shoes, and some breakfast (bless her heart), and we headed up to Seattle for the meet.

The meet began with the preliminaries of the jumping events (long, high, and triple) and throwing events (shot put, discus, and javelin). Each contestant got three attempts, and the top eight out of 16 would advance to the finals. Luke, clearly exhausted, scratched on his first two jumps, which meant he would need to hit a good one on his last attempt to make it into the finals. And, of course, he came through with a leap just good enough to advance.

After his first two jumps in the finals he was in third place – pretty impressive for somebody as tired as Luke, but not what we had come to expect from our amazing friend. As he was getting ready for his final jump, Mr. Daisy got Coach Preciado's attention and called her over to the stands. She then went and huddled with Luke.

"Luke, your dad gave me this to give to you," she said. "He thought it might be something you'd want to wear for your final jump."

She opened her hand and showed Luke what it was: Johnny's Special Olympics Gold Medal. Luke smiled, took that medal, and looked up in the stands where he found his dad. Mr. Daisy, who always said he never cared if we won or lost, just as long as we played fair and tried our hardest, gave Luke the thumbs-up sign. I think maybe deep down he did care if Luke won.

With that gold medal around his neck, Luke did something no high school kid in Washington had ever done: he triple jumped 50-feet. And with that leap he became the state champion.

The 880-yard preliminaries weren't until late afternoon, and I suggested to Luke that he find a place to lie down and take a nap. But he said no, that he needed to be cheering for all of his teammates. "I'll be able to get plenty of sleep tonight," he said.

The 880 was run in two different heats, and the top four finishers in each heat would advance to Saturday's finals, regardless of their time. Luke entered with the third best time in the state, but since your Friday time didn't matter, he ran as slowly as he possibly could and still be able to finish fourth in his heat to qualify for the finals. It was all about conserving energy.

But when we got to the track on Saturday, we were told that there was a problem. The meet director had decided that the finals should be made up of the eight runners with the best times in the preliminaries, not the top four finishers in each race. Coach Gallo was livid, and could not figure out how anybody thought it would be fair to change the rules in the middle of a competition.

But it became clear when we realized who the meet director was: Mr. Justin Case of Waterton, whose enmity towards Luke stretched back three years and had apparently not abated in the least. Fortunately the WIAA Director, the highly respected Mike Zech, was at the meet, and a meeting was hastily called to include all of the involved parties.

"Okay Justin, explain this to me please," Mr. Zech said.

"I just think it's more fair to have the eight boys with the eight fastest times compete in the finals, rather than the boys who finished in the top four in each race," Mr. Case explained. "Why should the kid who got fifth in the first heat be left out when he had a better time than the kid who finished fourth in the second heat?"

"Because that's the rule," Coach Gallo answered. "And that's always been the rule. You can't just go changing the rule because you think it's unfair."

"Let me see if I understand this right," Mr. Zech said. "Those boys ran their heats, knowing that their times wouldn't matter. But now, Justin, you are telling them that their times do matter. Is that right?"

"Well, yes," Mr. Case answered, somewhat sheepishly.

"And you think that's fair?" Mr. Zech asked incredulously.

"Yes."

"And who would be impacted by this incredibly brilliant decision?"

"It would mean Al Cahill of Waterton would be in the finals and Luke Daisy of Paul Revere would be out," one of the track officials answered.

"I see," Mr. Zech said, looking at Mr. Case and shaking his head. "Here's what we're going to do: we're going to follow the rules as they are written, as everyone understood them before the competition started. If you want to change the rules, Justin, you have to do it before the competition starts. I guess I assumed everybody understood that.

"But since that apparently seems wrong to you," he continued. "I'm afraid I'm going to have to ask you to step aside as meet director. It appears that you have some very questionable motives, or you're just plain insane. Either way, you have to go."

Mr. Case didn't say a word, just gave Luke and Coach Gallo a dirty look and stormed out of the room.

"Unbelievable," Mr. Zech said. "Luke, Tom: I'm sorry you had to go through this."

"No problem," Coach Gallo said. "Thank you for intervening."

As they went to leave, Mr. Zech added, "Good luck, Luke. I'm looking forward to watching you run."

And man-oh-man did he run.

Usually Luke hung back the first lap and then poured it on in the end. This time he went out strong and actually led when they had finished the first quarter-mile. I looked at my stop watch and couldn't believe what I was seeing. "Oh no, he's going too fast," I thought.

Boy was I wrong. He just kept moving like a powerful machine and won easily, breaking the state record in the process. And then an hour later, just for good measure, Luke anchored our mile relay foursome to another victory, and that win gave us the Class AAA state championship.

A lot of sports fans will remember the spring of 1973 as the time the great Secretariat won the Triple Crown in horse racing. I will always think of it as the time my amazing friend won seven (7!!!) state championships: team tennis, singles tennis, doubles tennis, team track, triple jump, 880, and mile relay.

Thanks to Luke Daisy, Paul Revere High School was going to need to invest in a much larger trophy case.

Chapter 38

Summer of '73

"There is nothing in the world so irresistibly contagious as laughter and good humor." – Charles Dickens

"You guys will not believe what happened yesterday!" Kenny exclaimed.

Luke, Ellie, and I looked up rather half-heartedly at our excited friend, who had just rolled himself into Oakwood Estates. It wasn't enough that Matthew Daisy had built our special tree mansion, now he had also installed a motorized ramp so that Kenny could come and go like the rest of us.

Our lack of enthusiasm at Kenny's excitement was simply because he started a lot of conversations that same way. Sometimes it was an amazing true story, but more times than not it was an amazing untrue story.

"You know how yesterday was the seventh of July," he went on. "The date was 7/7. And I looked in the paper and saw that the number 7 horse in the 7th race at Longacres racetrack was named *Lucky Seven*, and he was 7-1 odds. I figured this had to be a sign.

"So I took $77 out of my savings account and my sister drove me down there," he continued. "I bet $77 to win on number 7 in the 7th race at 7-1 odds on the date 7/7."

"Well?" I asked, as he paused for breath. Could my friend really have won almost $500? "Did he win?"

"No," Kenny answered sadly. "He got seventh."

We half-groaned, half-laughed.

That was life with Kenny Carew. He used to wonder aloud things like:

"How did the fool and his money get together in the first place?"

"What happens if you get scared half-to-death twice?"

"What was the greatest thing before sliced bread?"

"What if there were no hypothetical questions?"

"Whatever happened to Preparation A through G, and the first six Ups?"

"How does the snowplow driver get to work?"

"If the slipper fit Cinderella so well, how come it fell off when she ran out of the ball?"

"You know I love Shakespeare, but if 'all the world's a stage,' where is the audience supposed to sit?"

Indeed, all the world seemed to be a stage for Kenny, although sometimes he could get on our nerves with the endless jokes and stories.

"You know, Hoppy Bear," Ellie told him once, "you have the right to remain silent, even if you're not being arrested."

"I know he has the right to remain silent," I added. "I just don't think he has the ability."

Kenny just laughed and said, "I'm going to use both of those someday."

Sometimes, however, Kenny's questions were profound and the ensuing discussions memorable.

We were all at the Carews' house on a Sunday night in July for our weekly *Miss–n-Match* competition when one of those conversations took place. *Miss–n-Match* was a great category game that Mr. Carew had made up, and every Sunday evening throughout the summer we would gather at their house to battle it out. The weekly winner would get to take home the coveted *M-n-M Cup*, filled with real m&ms, and have their name logged in Mr. Carew's Official Book of Champions. Ellie and Mrs. Carew probably won the most, although each of us managed to claim victory at one time or another.

It was at the end of one of these games that Kenny broached a serious subject.

"Hey dad," he said, "should I be proud that I'm black?"

Mr. Carew paused, and we looked at him, curious what his answer would be.

"Why do you ask that, son?" he asked.

"Well, I keep hearing people talk about Black Pride, that we should have Black Pride, that we should know that we're special because we're black. Do you agree with that?"

Again Mr. Carew paused before answering.

"My answer to that is no," he said.

"No?" Kenny asked.

"Son, did you do anything to be black? No. That's the way you were created. Should Ellie be proud that she's white? Should

Luke be proud that he's tall? No. They didn't have anything to do with those things. It's how they were made.

"Pride can be a very tricky thing, son," he continued. "It can get you into a whole lot of trouble."

Then he turned to dad. "Am I saying that right, Robert?"

"I think so," dad answered. "But I think it's important for all of you kids to know where this whole Black Pride movement comes from. It's because for a very long time there have been a lot of people – some of them evil and some of them just sadly ignorant – that would have you believe that being black is somehow worse, or less important than being white. That's just very, very completely wrong!

"But I think what we should do is replace the word pride with gratefulness," he continued. "I think instead of being proud we should all be grateful for the way we were created.

"Scott?" he said, turning to Mr. Daisy.

"I'd say you guys hit the nail on the head," Luke's dad said. "The Bible says pride can lead to your downfall. I know all of us parents are so proud of you kids, but if we start puffing out our chests and saying 'look what a wonderful job we have done,' then we've missed the mark.

"So be proud of your family, be proud of your friends, be proud of your country, but be very careful about being proud of yourself. Like Robert said, be grateful, not proud."

"Does that make sense?" Mr. Carew asked.

"Yes," Kenny answered. "Although it's kind of hard to be proud of Mouse right now. He just got last place in *Miss-n-Match*, for crying out loud."

"And I'm very grateful that I just finished ahead of all three of my loser friends," Ellie added quickly.

Thus endeth our serious discussion. But all these years later it still sticks with me: gratitude instead of pride.

As the calendar turned from July to August, we got a couple pieces of very good news. The first was that Coach Jeego had been removed as head football and baseball coach.

Apparently Mr. Eilertson had called him into his office, and there waiting for him were a school board member and a union representative.

"Hugh, this is your official notification that I am relieving you of your head coaching duties," Mr. Eilertson announced.

"You can't do that," Coach Jeego responded.

"You wanna bet?" Mr. Eilertson said. "Read your contract, Hugh. It says that you serve as head coach at my discretion, and if I determine that your actions in that capacity are not beneficial to Paul Revere High School, I can have you removed."

He held up a large stack of papers.

"And I have here an awful lot of letters from parents, teachers, and other coaches that clearly indicate to me that your actions have not been beneficial to Paul Revere High School," he added.

Coach Jeego turned to his union rep. "Can he do that?" he asked.

"Yes, he most surely can."

"And you're not going to do anything to fight this?" Coach Jeego challenged.

"Hugh," the rep answered. "One of those letters is from me."

"And another one is from me," added the school board member.

"This does not impact your teaching duties, just your coaching," Mr. Eilertson concluded.

But Coach Jeego was not about to stay at Revere just to teach Physical Education and not coach. Instead, he got a job as the head football coach at Bickleton High School, a tiny class B school in central Washington. He wound up coaching there for 10 years, where every year his team lost about 4 or 5 games (because they "just weren't tough enough.")

Coach Hermansen, who had been our sophomore coach, was named as the head coach. In two years his teams had gone 18-and-0, and he was proving to be something of an offensive genius. And for the second time in three years, the legendary Harry Orr came out of retirement to be the head baseball coach.

The other piece of good news was that one of the top athletes in the state, Rick Evans, was transferring to Revere. Rick's dad had just retired after 30 years working at the Naval Shipyards in

Bremerton, and the family had moved to Bonney Flats to be closer to Mrs. Evans' aging parents. Rick was a star forward in basketball and pitcher in baseball.

Things were really starting to fall into place for our senior year.

The other thing that really kicked into full gear that summer before our final year of high school was the college recruiting of Luke. Every top football (Nebraska, Oklahoma, Alabama, etc.), basketball (UCLA, Indiana, Kentucky, etc.), and baseball (USC, Arizona State, Texas, etc.) program in the country was after him.

Luke told them all that he would not be making any decisions until his high school sports seasons were over. "I owe it to my school, my teammates, my coaches, and myself, not to be distracted," he said. "Please do not contact me until the final out in the final inning of our final baseball game."

Some schools did not take him at his word, and those were quickly eliminated from consideration. Other schools offered Luke a fancy car and the Daisy family a tidy sum of money. Those schools were eliminated even more quickly.

I tried to get Luke to give me an idea of which way he was leaning.

"Honestly, Mouse, I have no idea," he said. "I can't imagine moving away from my parents, or you and Kenny and Ellie. I hate to even think about it."

"Yeah, I know," I said. "I wish there were some way that we could all go somewhere together. But just because we head in different directions for college, doesn't mean we won't stay best friends our whole life."

"I think that's a guarantee," he agreed.

"When the time comes, I know you'll make the right decision," I said.

"I know it sounds crazy, but I'm still hoping for some place where I can play all three sports."

"Well if anybody can do it, it would be you."

"Thanks," he said. "And I won't make any decision without talking to you first. I'll definitely need to know what you think I should do."

Now it was my turn to say "thanks."

"But how about if we don't think about it, and just go out and win a bunch of games," he smiled. "I think it's time for you to hop on the state championship train."

"Yeah, I like that idea. I like it a lot."

Chapter 39

<u>Senior Year</u>

"Consult not your fears, but your hopes and your dreams." –
Pope John XXIII

Before football season started a sportswriter from the Seattle Times, Dan Davis, did a feature story on Luke, and asked him about his goals for the upcoming year.

"My goal is for us to go undefeated in football and win the state championship, undefeated in basketball and win the state championship, and undefeated in baseball and win the state championship," Luke answered without hesitation.

"Isn't that kind of cocky," Mr. Davis asked him.

"No. It's only cocky if I tell you we're going to do that," Luke answered. "I'm not making a prediction, or giving a guarantee. I'm just telling you what our goal is. I know it's as lofty as it can be, but I really think we have the athletes and the coaches to make it happen. My hope is that, in coming years, when people talk about the greatest high school class in Washington state sports history they will have to include the 1974 Paul Revere Minutemen.

"Look, we could go out and lose our first football game," he continued. "That doesn't mean we'd give up on the whole season. We would just have to reset our goals."

"What about individual goals?" Davis asked.

"Nope."

"None?"

"Well, I hope to play well and stay healthy. But no statistical goals. The problem with individual statistical goals is they can get in the way of team goals. Let's say I set a goal to average a certain amount of points per game in basketball. Maybe then I'd take some bad shots that wouldn't help the team win."

"So it's all about winning?"

"No. It's all about trying your best, playing fair, being a good teammate, having fun, and making lifetime memories," Luke said. And then he added with a smile, "And winning."

It didn't take long for us to realize that football with Coach Hermansen in charge would be vastly different from football with Coach Jeego in charge. For one thing, he believed in a wide-open offense that included a lot of passing, different formations, audibles, and trick plays. "Fast and Fun" was his offensive philosophy.

But the main difference was that he permitted Clark Kent to take off his suit and tie and glasses and be the super hero he was intended to be. Luke, who had finally stopped growing at 6-foot-4, 220 pounds, would be our quarterback on offense, rover on defense, punt & kick returner, and long-snapper on punts and extra points. (Contrary to what some people might have believed, he did not drive the bus to our away games, or clean up the locker room after home games.) Basically, Coach Hermansen said "lead the way Luke." And we were more than happy to follow.

Our junior year I caught a total of 9 passes. Our senior year I caught 9 passes in the first game. Our junior year we averaged 10 points a game. Our senior year we averaged 10 points a quarter. The writer Dan Davis suggested that our name Minutemen was a reference to how quickly we could score.

At a time when the average high school football score was probably 14-7, we were flying up and down the field and scoring almost at will. We won our first game 42-14, our second game 35-7, and our third game 48-20. Coach Hermansen was so far ahead of his time, nobody knew how to defend us. Sometimes we operated out of the shotgun formation. Sometimes we used a no-huddle offense. Our playbook included reverses, double reverses, halfback passes, and even a Statue of Liberty.

One play against Waterton Luke handed it off to our star running back, Blake Harvey, who stopped and pitched it back to Luke. Luke then took off around the left end, but lateralled it to me coming around to the right. After about 10 yards I stopped and passed it back to Luke who had circled around the left side and was wide open. Unfortunately, my pass fell way short. (Hey, I was a receiver, not a quarterback.) Still, it was a pretty cool play, and we ended up trouncing our formerly-feared rivals, 49-0.

Meanwhile, on the other side of the state, Patrick Henry High School of Spokane was winning with defense. They were ranked number 1 in the state and we were ranked number 2. And just like us, they were wiping out every opponent. The Patriots hadn't yielded a touchdown in the last two seasons, and hadn't lost a game in the last 3. It looked very much like we were on a collision course during what would be the first-ever Washington state high school football playoffs.

Sure enough, both teams finished undefeated and cruised through the first two playoff games. We were 11-and-0 and had scored 450 points. They were 11-and-0 and had not given up a single point. It was the classic irresistible force versus the immovable object. Something would have to give.

The state championship game was scheduled for Saturday, November 24 at Husky Stadium on the University of Washington campus. Because it was the first-ever state playoffs, the Seattle Times actually held a press conference on the Wednesday before the game, interviewing both coaches and a player from each team.

Coach Hermansen and their Coach Epperson of course said all the right things: total respect for opponent, the need to rise to the occasion, excited about this opportunity, etc. But their player spokesman had apparently not been schooled in what *not* to say, or had chosen to ignore any advice he had been given.

Mack Haroni was their two-time all-state middle linebacker, headed to Notre Dame on a full-ride football scholarship. Nicknamed "Mad Dog" because of his wild-eyed, ferocious style of play, he was not about to show any respect for us. His tone was angry and condescending.

"Hey, we have not given up a single point all year, and we are not about to start now," he said. "I know they've scored a bunch this year, but they haven't played anybody good. We will destroy them."

"Is that a guarantee?" one of the sportswriters asked.

"You bet it is," Mad Dog responded.

And then the sportswriter asked Luke if he was willing to guarantee a victory.

"Of course not," Luke answered. "I don't know if we're going to win. How can anyone know who is going to win? We haven't played each other, and we haven't played any of the same teams to compare. All I know is that we'll come out and do our best. I'm pretty sure they'll be the best team we've played all year, and I'm guessing we might be the best team that they've played."

Mad Dog scoffed. "What kind of a leader are you if you don't even have confidence in your own team?" he spat out.

Luke turned and looked at him, kind of bemused. You could tell he was debating about whether or not to respond to the insult.

"I guess you'd have to ask my teammates what kind of a leader I am," he said. "But I do know it takes no courage and no brains, obviously, to guarantee a victory. And I know that I don't need to be taking leadership lessons from someone with a double-digit IQ."

Mad Dog glared at Luke and then snarled, "You're dead meat!"

At our practice later, I asked Luke if he thought it was a good idea to talk to Haroni like that.

"People who play with that much anger often make mistakes," he said. "I figured it might be good to rile him up a little.

"But I was a little bit nervous that he was going to bite me," he smiled. "I hope he's been checked for rabies. There seemed to be a lot of foam around his mouth."

There were 30,000 people in Husky Stadium for the game, and I'm sure most of them were expecting a close, hard-fought contest.

They were wrong.

Luke was at his best level 3 performance ("Holy cow did you see that?!") from the opening kickoff, and like some kind of anti-gravitational force lifted the rest of us up there with him. He ran for two touchdowns and threw for two more, one of them a perfect 40-yard spiral that hit me in full stride as I crossed the goal line and managed not to drop it. He also intercepted two passes, and just so he could say he did something that he hadn't done all year, he blocked a punt.

The team that hadn't given up a single point all year yielded 35, and Paul Revere High School celebrated a dominating 35-14 victory to become the first-ever Washington state high school football champions.

Haroni, of course, was nowhere to be found during the post-game handshakes. Bullies are like that.

"I guess maybe old Mad Dog is in the doghouse," Luke quipped.

Basketball season was more of the same. Win after win after win. Now that we had Rick Evans, teams could not double-team Luke. We also had a sharp-shooting junior named Levi Jackson, and a good big man with the lyrical name Bob Traub. Bob had grown 3 inches in the last year and was now 6-foot-6. Rounding out the starting 5 was yours truly. My job was to set screens, try to play good defense, come up with an occasional rebound, and try not to miss my lay-in when I led the team out onto the court for warm-ups. I only scored in double figures one time, but that was fine with me. Between football with Coach Hermansen and basketball with Coach Wagon, I was having the time of my life.

And just like football, the state championship game came down to the ultimate clash of the titans. We were 26-and-0 and ranked number 1 in the state, and John Adams High School of Seattle was also 26-and-0 and ranked number 2 in the state.

The championship game was scheduled for Saturday, March 16, in the Coliseum, which seemed quite an appropriate venue for this battle of gladiators. The Seattle Center Coliseum opened in 1962 as part of the wonderful World's Fair. In August of '64 it was the site of back-to-back sold-out Beatles concerts, for those who could afford the $5 ticket price. And starting in October of 1967, it was the home of our beloved Seattle Supersonics.

On this night a capacity crowd of 14,000 filled the place, all expecting and hoping for a great game.

Trust me, nobody left disappointed.

Adams, with three players who would go on to play Division 1 college basketball, came out on fire and built an 8-point lead after the first quarter. We battled back in the second quarter and the teams went into the locker room at halftime tied, 36-36.

From that point on nobody led by more than four points. At the end of regulation time we were trailing, 70-68, when Luke hit a 20-foot jumper at the buzzer to send the game into overtime.

At the end of the first overtime Luke sank two free throws with 3 seconds left to send the game into a second overtime.

We were about to win the game in the second overtime when a kid from Adams, Cameron Globe, made a shot from near half-court at the buzzer.

By this time, several players from both teams had fouled out, including Rick Evans and Bob Traub for us. Those of us that were left were getting exhausted. Even Luke, who had played every second of the game, was breathing harder than I'd ever seen.

At the end of the third overtime we were again trailing by two points when Adams fouled Travis Grady with one second left on the clock. Travis was a sophomore who would go on to be a great player, but he had spent most of the season on the junior varsity and was in the game because of all the players who had fouled out. He was so nervous he looked like he might pass out.

Luke walked up to him at the free throw line before the ref handed him the ball and said, "Travis, you know what happens if you miss these free throws, right?"

Travis gulped and nodded his head.

"That's right," Luke continued. "We'll have to run extra lines on Monday."

Then he smiled and ruffled up Travis's hair. Travis swished both shots, and we headed into the fourth overtime.

Halfway through the fourth overtime Coach Wagon called timeout because he could see how completely depleted Luke was. He had now played 46 minutes without a break, his jersey was completely soaked through, and it looked like he might fall over.

As the timeout drew to a close and it was about time to head back onto the floor, Luke looked up at me and shook his head.

"I don't know if I can do this, Mouse," he said. "I'm not ready to go back out there."

I knew we were out of timeouts, and I knew we didn't have a chance without Luke on the floor. So I did something that I'm not particularly proud of. Well, maybe a little.

I picked up the container that held all of our water bottles and loosened the lids on all 12 of them. Then I told our manager, Fred Behrmann, that he needed to take the water and trip and spill it on the court, but to make sure it looked like an accident.

Fred, who we all loved, gave me a quizzical look, but I said, "Trust me on this."

Bless his heart, Fred nodded, picked up the container, turned and did a prat fall that even Kenny would have been proud of. He even let out a big "oof" as he went down. All of the plastic water bottles crashed to the floor and water spilled all over. It took about 5 minutes to get it all dried up.

The extra time is what Luke needed. "Okay, let's go," he said.

Now at the end of the fourth overtime we had the ball, trailing by 2 points with 10 seconds left. With Rick out of the game, Luke was now being double-teamed, so he passed me the ball on the baseline for a wide open 8-footer to tie the game.

I could make that shot 9 out of 10 times, but as I went up to take the shot a strange thing happened. All of a sudden the basketball felt like a medicine ball. It's funny how nerves can make your body do strange things. As soon as I released it I knew it was going to be short, probably an air ball. My heart sank.

The Adams player jumping up to grab the rebound and secure the win also thought it was going to be an air ball. But miracle of miracles, the ball actually hit the front of the rim, deflected off their would-be rebounder's fingers, and right back to me. I quickly passed it to Luke as if we were playing hot potato, and he calmly made the basket as the buzzer sounded. We were headed into overtime number five.

As the fifth overtime drew to a close, we were behind by 1 point with 16 seconds left. Coach Wagon called timeout and set up a play designed for Luke to take the final shot as time expired. There would be no sixth overtime. This was it, do or die.

As we came out of the timeout, Luke put his arm around my shoulders.

"Listen Mouse," he said. "They all know that the ball is coming to me. They will be all over me. So how do you get into the house if the front door is locked?"

I looked at him sideways, like maybe exhaustion was making him incoherent.

"You go through the back door, Mouse," he said, smiling and nodding. "The back door, baby." I still wasn't sure what he was talking about.

So we inbounded the ball to Levi who brought the ball up court, and then Travis and I set a double pick for Luke to pop out and get the ball at the top of the key.

Eight seconds left.

Luke was double-teamed. He jab-stepped right, brought the ball between his legs, one hard dribble left and then a cross-over to split the defenders.

Four seconds left.

As Luke elevated for his shot near the foul line, Adams' 6-foot-8-inch center ran and leaped at him. Everyone, including me and the guy who was guarding me, just stopped to watch and see if Luke could get the ball over the outstretched hand of the defender. It was like it was all happening in slow motion.

And then something in my brain clicked. Luke's words. *"The back door."*

Suddenly I broke towards the basket, just as Luke ducked under the charging defender. A back door cut like we had done so many times in all the years we had been playing together. His bounce pass hit me perfectly in stride and I rose up for the lay-in. I don't know why the ball didn't feel like a medicine ball, or why my adrenaline didn't cause me to slam the ball off the backboard. But it left my hand, rolling gently off my fingers, off the glass, and in.

Buzzer. Game over.

Paul Revere 90, John Adams 89, five overtimes. We were the 1974 Washington state high school basketball champions.

Our screaming fans piled out of the stands to mob us. Some of our buddies actually lifted me up on their shoulders for a few seconds. It felt surreal. Kind of nice, but kind of wrong. I may have played a bigger role than usual in this episode, but in this Dynamic Duo there was only one Caped Crusader, and everyone knew that was Luke. There were so many reasons we won, including Travis making those free throws, Fred spilling the water, and my shot at the end. But I think Luke's 44 points might have been a bit of a factor as well. (Remember, this was before the 3-point shot had been added.)

Still, Luke kept insisting on giving me more than the credit I deserved in the post-game interviews.

"What a play by Mouse!" he said. "There's no way I could have made the shot over that guy. Mouse had to think fast and move to get open, and then he had to make that high pressure basket. But I had no doubt that he would come through for us. He always does."

A reporter asked me how it felt to be a hero. "Well, there is a hero in this room all right," I said. "A superhero. But it sure isn't me."

One of the reporters told Luke that a player from Adams had said that he thought we had gotten lucky, and that they could beat us 9 out of 10 times.

Luke shook his head. "If we played them 10 times we'd all be dead," he said.

When Luke took off his shoes (actually he asked me to take them off because he could hardly move after playing all 52 minutes), I could hardly believe it. Both of his socks were soaked with blood where blisters had rubbed raw and burst. I just had to shake my head and smile at his incredible toughness.

"Yeah, I might need to get a new pair of socks," he said.

Two down and one to go.

We were only going to have one day to rest and enjoy our basketball championship before baseball started on Monday. Fortunately, the western Washington skies opened up and poured three straight days of rain on us, so the start of practice was delayed until Thursday. It was the first time I could remember being thankful for our abundance of northwest rain.

Coach Orr, now 67, had the energy and enthusiasm of a man 20 years younger. He loved baseball, he loved kids, and he loved coaching. And he loved that he had the chance to win one more championship.

Mr. Daisy joked of his friend, "He's great at coaching. He just seems to be not so great at retiring from coaching."

"Well, if we win it all this year," Coach Orr said, "I can retire again, and maybe this one will take."

We hated to deprive future Paul Revere High School baseball players of the joy of playing for Coach Orr, but we definitely wanted to help him go out on top.

Coach Orr had several sayings that pretty well defined his baseball philosophy:

"Swing hard. You just might hit it."

"Drawing a walk is like mushy cereal. Getting a hit is like crisp bacon. Swing the bat!"

"Hit the ball hard, run like a deer."

"It's better to go down swinging at a bad pitch than strike out just gazing at a good one."

Sure enough, being aggressive at the plate and playing with a delightful exuberance, we won and won and won some more. It helped that Rick Evans was every bit as good of a pitcher as he was a basketball player, and it really helped that nobody seemed to be able to get Luke out.

We made it to the state championship game, where we came up against an old friend. Another school in our league, Brookfield, had made it to the title game as well, and their coach was our wonderful third grade teacher and junior high baseball coach, Mr. Scott Stokes.

The championship game was scheduled for Saturday, May 25, at Cheney Stadium in Tacoma, home of the Class AAA Tacoma Twins. Before the game Coach Stokes announced that he had no intention of having his team pitch to Luke.

"Listen, nobody has more respect for Luke than I do," he explained. "And I know there will be a lot of people at the game who want to watch him bat. I love to watch him bat. But as the coach of Brookfield it's my job to do everything I can to help us win. I've seen him do too many amazing things. I just can't let him beat us. I'm sorry. A lot of people have wound up losing because they underestimated Luke. I am not going to be one of them."

And so they intentionally walked Luke with two outs and nobody on base in the first inning.

And then they intentionally walked him with runners on first and second and nobody out in the third inning.

And then they intentionally walked him with one out and nobody on base in the fifth inning.

As we came to the bottom of the seventh and last inning, Brookfield led 1-0, and Luke was slated to bat fifth. Coach Stokes was praying for a 1-2-3 inning, or at worst two outs with an empty base so he could walk Luke again.

Their ace pitcher, Tom Mehawk, had given up only four hits while striking out 12. Things did not look good for the

Minutemen, especially when Mehawk started the inning by striking out our number eight hitter. But then he threw a slider that didn't break, and our number 9 hitter headed to first base with a hit-by-pitch.

Our leadoff hitter, Kirk Schweitzer, followed with a perfect bunt down the third base line to move the runner to second, but when their catcher and third baseman went to field the ball they tripped over each other, and both runners were safe.

I batted second in the lineup, so now it was my turn to bat, with Luke on deck. I fully expected to get the bunt sign from Coach Orr to move the runners over, but he just looked at me and gave me the "swing away" sign.

"Michael," he hollered. "Swing hard. You just might hit it."

Our wise old coach knew that if I sacrificed the runners over to second and third, then Coach Stokes would be able to walk Luke intentionally again. Our best bet was to hope that somehow I could reach base and force the other team's hand. I did have one of our team's four hits, although it was a check swing blooper that barely dropped over the first baseman's glove. Not exactly a Henry Aaron-like screaming line drive.

I stepped to the plate, but had to quickly back out and grab a towel. My hands were so sweaty that I think the bat would have gone flying if I had tried to swing.

"Mouse," Luke said as I got ready to step back into the batter's box. "Hit the ball hard, run like a deer."

And so I swung hard at the first pitch. I didn't hit it hard, but I did run like a deer. The ball went straight down and bounced right off the plate, straight up in the air. And I mean high up in the air. By the time it came down into the catcher's mitt, one foot in front of home plate, I was safe at first and the bases were loaded. I had just come through with what might have been the shortest hit in high school history, about 12 inches.

And now Coach Stokes faced a real dilemma. His plan to walk Luke every time had paid off, but now it would mean forcing in the tying run with only one out, hoping to get the next two hitters out and move to extra innings.

He took a long, slow walk out to the mound to talk to his pitcher, who seemed to be arguing his case to pitch to Luke. But Coach Stokes vetoed that plan and opted to issue Luke a bases loaded intentional walk. I doubt if anyone had ever seen that before. I suppose it might have happened during Babe Ruth's heyday.

So the catcher stood up and put his right hand out, the signal for Mehawk to throw an intentional ball way outside. Luke rested the bat on his shoulder, resigned to another missed opportunity to swing the bat.

But just before the pitch Luke stole a glance into the Brookfield dugout and caught a glimpse of Coach Stokes subtly indicating for his right fielder to move back a couple of steps. Luke recognized the ploy to fool him into taking a strike, and then being able to pitch to him ahead in the count.

As the pitcher started his delivery the catcher jumped back in his stance, and Luke went from being nonchalant to coiled and ready to strike. Mehawk's fastball came in at about 85 miles per hour. It left at about 100.

Luke's only swing of the game produced a royal blast that carried over the right field fence for a grand slam home run and a 4-1 victory, and just like that we were the state baseball champions.

After our on-field celebration, with the obligatory pig-pile at home plate, Coach Stokes was the first one to congratulate Luke.

"How could you do that to your old teacher and coach?" he asked, giving Luke a hug and pat on the back.

"Sorry coach," Luke said. "I knew you couldn't bring yourself to walk in the tying run."

"Well, I sure wish I had."

Undefeated in football and state champions.

Undefeated in basketball and state champions.

Undefeated in baseball and state champions.

The Paul Revere High School class of '74 had just accomplished what no other class before or since could do. The amazing Luke Daisy had set the goal, and then the amazing Luke Daisy had led the way.

Chapter 40

The Legend

"Heroes are remembered. Legends never die." — Babe Ruth, The Sandlot

I hate to brag, but I made it onto the cover of *Sports Illustrated*. It's the June 8, 1974 edition.

Back in the 60s and 70s the great sports magazine would have an issue where they would pick the high school athlete of the year for the whole country, and he would be featured on the cover under the banner *Best Schoolboy Athlete*.

In 1974 their choice was Luke Daisy, of course, and the cover photo showed him about to cross home plate, arms raised, giant smile on his face, after he'd just homered to win the state championship for us. Waiting there to greet him in celebration are all of his teammates, and if you look closely you can see the back of my number 14 jersey and my right leg. Hey, it counts.

The great writer Frank Deford did the story on Luke, and I still remember how it started:

"Superman, Spiderman, and Batman. Hercules, Achilles, and Odysseus. Paul Bunyan and Pecos Bill.

Trust me when I tell you that I am familiar with all of their stories, and I know that none of them are actually true. They are the stuff of comic books, Greek mythology, and tall tales. I know the difference between reality and fantasy.

Because unless you live in or around Bonney Flats, Washington, you may be tempted to think the following story about Luke Daisy is one of those fun but fictional frolics.

But you would be wrong."

He then went on to include most, but not all, of Luke's sports accomplishments: the hole-in-one as an 8-year-old; the Little League World Series heroics; the national Pass, Punt, & Kick championship; the 11 high school state championships (4 in track & field, 3 in tennis, 2 in baseball, and 1 in football and basketball), including both track and tennis in the same sports season; and the 6 First-Team All-State selections (2 each in football, basketball, and baseball).

I was there to witness all of it, and I still almost had trouble believing it.

Just about everyone in Bonney Flats bought a copy of that *Sports Illustrated* issue, and I bet Luke was asked to sign them all.

"It's kind of weird," he said. "I played the whole year without getting hurt, but now I don't think I could even throw a baseball. With all that signing, my hand is killing me."

"Well, you'd better get used to it," I offered.

Our graduation ceremony was the following Saturday, June 15, and the four of us – *The Fantastic Four* – were among the first of the 400 to gladly accept our diplomas from Paul Revere High School. The diplomas were handed out alphabetically, so Kenny (Carew) was first of us to get his, and he rolled across the stage in record speed, adding a fancy spin move at the end, much to the delight of the crowd. I was next (Cateere), followed by Luke (Daisy), then Ellie (Fent). Dad had gotten three extra wheel chairs from his office, so the three of us also rolled across the stage in support of our dear friend. Anyone who didn't know better might have thought there had been some kind of freak accident, or else we were making fun of Kenny. We would have had to explain to them how much we loved our crazy friend, and that it was actually his idea.

"It's not fair that I get to have all the fun," he explained. "We should all roll through this thing together."

I had been hoping to be the class Valedictorian, but I wound up second in the class behind Ellie. We both recorded perfect 4.0 Grade Point Averages, but somehow the A's she got in her *Advanced Microbiology* and *Calculus* classes were weighted higher than my A's in *Beginning Guitar* and *Introduction to Cooking* classes. Go figure.

Kenny was chosen as the class speaker, and he had the entire audience in the palm of his hands. He talked about the importance of holding onto your dreams. "Unless, like me," he said, "you have a recurring dream about being chased through the woods by a peanut butter sandwich." Despite his physical struggles, I don't think anybody who really knew our Hoppy doubted that he would achieve his real dreams.

I had decided to go to the University of Washington and major in political science, with the idea that I would follow it up with law school, and then see where life took me.

Kenny was heading off to UCLA on a full-ride scholarship from their Performing Arts Department, where he would pursue a Bachelor of Fine Arts degree in Television & Film Production. Of course that's not what he told people.

"I got my freshman class schedule, and I have Psychology, Biology, Geology, and Physiology," he would say. "I'm planning to be an *ologist*."

My dad told Ellie that he had made some contacts and she would also be attending the University of Washington, as a pre-med student.

"But Dr. Cateere," she objected. "I can't afford college."

"No. But we can," dad told her. "I always kind of figured my son would follow in my footsteps and become a doctor, but he has chosen a different path. So I guess it's up to my *daughter* - that's you - to follow that course."

I had told dad about our Oakwood Estates conversation years ago concerning our future plans, with Ellie's dream to be a doctor.

"But I can't let you do that," Ellie said.

"Of course you can," dad answered. "Mrs. Cateere and I had always wanted a daughter, a younger sister for Michael, but that wasn't to be. And then God brought you into all of our lives, Ellie. And I know Michael certainly doesn't think of you as a sister, but we think of you as the daughter we never had."

It didn't surprise me to see dad crying. He was a self-described big crybaby. But as they hugged, I realized it was the first time I had ever seen Ellie cry.

Luke's decision was a much harder one, and it became more complicated when the Cleveland Indians made him the fourth player chosen in the Major League baseball draft, just after Lonnie Smith of the Philadelphia Phillies and just before Dale Murphy of the Atlanta Braves. The experts said he would have been the top pick if teams were sure he would choose baseball over football and basketball. He said he was going to announce his decision on Independence Day because he loved the date: 7/4/74.

A couple days after graduation the four of us headed to Wimpy's for some pizza, figuring we needed to make the most of what little time the four of us had together before our paths diverged. Just before we were finishing and getting ready to leave, in walked Bruce Junkers and his buddy Mitch Templeton.

Junkers had gone off to Washington State University on a baseball scholarship a couple of years earlier, but had gotten suspended from the team as a freshman when he was caught drinking, stealing from some of the rooms in his dormitory, and beating up another student who threatened to turn him in.

The next year he got kicked out of school entirely for assaulting a female student. The story we heard of what he had done to her was really awful, but his dad had pulled some strings so that he didn't get charged. Since returning to Bonney Flats he lived back in his dad's basement, tried to sell cars at his dad's lot, and spent an awful lot of time drinking and causing trouble.

And here he was again, clearly drunk, as he marched up to our table. Mitch just stood aside, smirking.

"Well, well, well," Junkers slurred. "If it isn't Puke Pansy and his loser friends."

We just looked up at him and kind of shook our heads. I could see there was no anger in Luke; more pity than anything.

"Hey Bruce," Ellie said. "We're about to leave, but we have some extra pizza here. You and Mitch are welcome to it."

Bruce just glared at her. I don't think he was used to anybody being nice to him unless they were afraid. Clearly Ellie was not afraid.

"It's good pizza," she said. "We're just all full. You guys help yourself."

You could tell Bruce was a bit flummoxed by this and he didn't quite know what to do. But eventually he decided to resort to his natural ways, and with his arm swept the pizza off the table and onto the floor.

"That's what I think of your lousy pizza," he spat out.

"Come on, let's just go," I said, and we all got up to leave.

But as we slid out of the booth and stood, we found out Bruce wasn't done.

"Hey Pansy," he said. "I heard your retard brother finally died."

Now Luke stopped, and the look in his eye changed to one of unrestrained anger and impending violence. I really thought this might be the end of Bruce Junkers.

"Luke," I said, trying to get his attention as he stared at Bruce.

"Luke," I said louder, but still my voice didn't register.

"Luke!" I yelled, grabbing his arm, and he turned to me and his eyes came back into focus.

"What would Johnny say if he was here?" I implored. "You know he would say: 'Luke, don't hurt him.' Listen, he's just trying to goad you so that Mitch over there can report it and you will get in all kinds of trouble.

"Look at him, Luke," I continued. "He is not worth it."

Finally Luke nodded, lowered his head and walked past Bruce towards the exit. Kenny and Ellie followed. Now it was just Bruce sneering at me.

But as I went to walk past him, something happened inside of me that had never happened before. It's kind of hard to describe. It was like when you pour a can of Coke into a glass too fast, and pretty soon the foam is rising up rapidly and you know you can't stop it, and it's going to completely flow out of the glass, like a volcano with lava pouring out of it, and there's nothing you can do to prevent it. That's what this felt like, only it wasn't foam and it wasn't lava. It was unadulterated rage.

I was 18 ½ years old and for the first time in my life I punched someone. With every ounce of strength I had, fueled by every ounce of built-up anger inside of me, for Johnny and for Luke and for all of the other kids who had been harassed and harmed by this bully, I let him have it. My fist connected with his jaw and he went down fast and hard. The contact was so loud – and I'm not sure, but I may have also let out some kind of a banshee wail – my three friends stopped in their tracks and turned around to see what had happened.

I looked over at Mitch, and apparently there was still murder in my eyes, because he looked wide-eyed and terrified, turned and ran.

When we got out to my car I was still in a high state of emotional tension.

"Are you okay, Mouse?" Luke asked.

"Yeah, let's just take a few minutes to calm down," Ellie added.

It took several minutes but I was finally able to breathe calmly again, and my heart rate returned to normal.

"Hey Mouse," Luke said. "What happened to 'What would Johnny say?' What happened to 'Don't hurt him Luke?' What was that all about?"

"I don't know," I answered. "I'm not really sure what happened to me. But how come you never told me how much it hurts to punch somebody in the jaw? My hand is killing me."

"Frankly," Luke said, "I didn't think that was something you would ever need to know."

"You know what, Mouse," Kenny added from the back seat. "I think we're going to have to start calling you Rocky."

"You mean because I punch like Rocky Marciano?" I asked.

"No," he said. "Because you're so squirrelly."

Luke agonized over his decision, asked what I thought he should do, and sought the advice of Coach Hermansen, Coach Wagon, and Coach Orr, as well as his family.

"Man, Luke, I haven't seen you this nervous since you had to invite a girl to the ninth grade dance," I said. "And that worked out pretty well, right?"

"Well this is just a bit more serious, don't you think, Mouse?" he answered.

He was especially worried about his mom if he decided to go far from home. Johnny's death had taken so much out of her.

"Dad, I just can't decide," he told Mr. Daisy. "I keep thinking: what if I make the wrong choice?"

Finally his dad smiled, put his arm around Luke and said, "Son, you're way too worried about this. The truth is you can't make the wrong decision. Whatever you decide will be right."

"How do you know that, dad?" Luke asked.

"Because I've seen how hard you've been praying about it, and I know how the rest of us have been praying about it. And I know what it says in Proverbs 3: 'Trust in the Lord with all your heart … and He *WILL* direct your paths.' God can use you to do great things whatever you choose and wherever you go.

"Nobody knows what the future holds. But we know who holds the future."

And so Luke relaxed and made his decision. "I think maybe part of me was afraid that I would make the wrong decision and regret it for the rest of my life," he said. "Now I just feel a peace and a confidence that this will be right for me."

The day before Luke was set to make his announcement, he and I were having a late-night milk shake at Bluto's. They were the best.

"Man, I am really going to miss this place," Luke said.

"Yeah, we'll have to make a plan to meet here at least once a year for the rest of our lives, you, me, Ellie, and Kenny," I answered.

"I like it," Luke said.

"Closing time, boys. Sorry," the manager said, poking his head around the corner. Bluto's closed at 9 p.m., but the manager, a wonderful man named Steven Edwards, always let us hang around longer. We would often help him clean up and straighten all the tables and chairs, and he knew how much we loved to just sit and talk. Tonight, like so many nights, we were the last two left in the place.

"Thank you, Mr. Edwards," Luke said. "You need us to help with anything?"

"No thanks, guys," he said. "I've got it covered. Maybe I'll see you tomorrow night."

I checked my watch as we headed out to my car and noticed that it was exactly 10:10, my favorite time: like getting two perfect scores. It's funny the things you remember.

"Rats. I forgot my coat," Luke said, and turned to head back inside. "And by the way, your shoes are untied."

"I'm not falling for that," I said.

Luke just smiled and pointed down. Sure enough, both of my shoes were untied.

So I bent down in the middle of the parking lot to tie my shoes as Luke went in to get his coat. I heard the revving engine and the squealing tires but took a second to process what I was hearing. By the time I stood up and saw the car barreling down on me it was too late to jump out of the way, so I closed my eyes and braced myself for the collision.

The impact was jarring, only it didn't come from the front, it came from the side. It wasn't the speeding car that hit me, it was Luke. He hit me with a flying tackle and knocked me out of the way just before the car ran me over. I hit the ground hard, hurt but safe. I was going to be okay.

Luke was not.

The car had hit him full force, and his head hit the cement with a sickening thud. I looked up in time to see the car peeling out and spinning onto the highway. Although the headlights were not on and I did not see a license plate, I could clearly see the car's cherry red side panel as it passed under the street light.

I limped over to Luke, who was lying flat on his back, his eyes open and lifeless. I sat down and gently lifted up his shoulders and cradled his head in my lap. I don't remember any of the words that spilled out of my mouth as I willed my amazing friend back to life.

Mr. Edwards had heard the sounds of the crash and the speeding car, rushed outside to see what had happened, and then called for an ambulance and the police.

It's strange the things that run through your mind when your world comes crashing down. When the ambulance crew took Luke away, I remember wondering if all the blood would come out of my jeans. As if it, or anything else, would ever matter again.

I remember wishing there had been some profound last words between us, and not "your shoes are untied." For the rest of my life I have wondered: what if my shoes hadn't been untied?

Mostly, as the ambulance door closed and they drove away, I remember thinking: I will never get to thank my best friend for saving my life.

Chapter 41

<u>Aftermath</u>

"You can go your whole life collecting days, and none will outweigh the one you wish you had back." – Mitch Albom, For One More Day

The next several days passed in a blur. Our family, the Carews, Ellie, and all of the Daisy family hunkered down together in our house. It was like the entire city had gone into shock as news spread, but then everybody rallied with an outpouring of support for Luke's family. People brought enough food to feed an army or two, but I hardly even remember eating anything. Rain drenched the region for two straight days, and the city of Bonney Flats cancelled their Independence Day fireworks show. I doubt if many people would have attended anyway.

I told the police what I had seen, and that I had no doubt about the car that killed Luke. It was Bruce Junkers' 1974 Chevy Camaro.

But when they went to the Junkers home the day after the accident, Mr. Junkers, Bruce, and his buddy Mitch all swore that Bruce had been home all night, and the front of his car had been damaged where he had crashed into a tree next to the family driveway earlier that afternoon. They just hadn't had time to report it to the insurance company. Sure enough, the car was still rammed up against the tree. It was an airtight alibi, and since I had not seen a license plate, and there were no other witnesses, there was nothing the police could do. The case would go unsolved.

I really don't know who Bruce had intended to run down, Luke or me, since the parking lot was dark and he didn't have his lights on. But I did know that he was going to get away with it.

Sometimes the bad guy wins.

The funeral was held the following Saturday, attended by about 5,000 people, not just from Bonney Flats but from around the state, and even other parts of the country, including several of the coaches who had recruited Luke.

Later I found out that Tom Osborne, Nebraska's outstanding football coach and one of the classiest men college sports has ever known, had sent a large check to the Daisy family to cover any expenses that they might have. Luke had not even committed to Nebraska, but Coach Osborne had been so impressed with him that he felt compelled to help. Somebody asked him if it might be some kind of an NCAA rules infraction and he said, "I don't know, and I really don't care." You have to admire people who decide to do good things regardless of the consequences they might face.

Mr. Daisy asked me if I would deliver the eulogy since I knew Luke better than anyone. I wasn't sure if I could get through it, but I agreed to try. I don't remember all of what I said, but I don't think I mentioned even one thing that Luke had accomplished on the field. I talked about his faith, his tenderness with Johnny, his toughness in standing up to bullies, and his unwavering support for his friends. I talked about his great courage, except for when he had to ask a girl to the dance. And I talked about how I owed him, not just my lifetime nickname of Mouse, but my very life itself.

Kenny sang a song he had written, called *"I'll Give My Life."* It was based on the words of Jesus from John 15:13: *"Greater love has no one than this, that he lay down his life for his friends."* For someone who was the best at making people laugh, Kenny made an awful lot of people cry that day.

Mrs. Daisy never played the piano again. Dad assured me that, medically, you can't die from a broken heart, but there was no doubt that losing both Johnny and Luke was more than her tender heart could handle. Two years later, she was gone too.

I know that none of us really know just what heaven is going to be like. It says in I Corinthians 2 that "no eye has seen, no ear has heard, no mind has conceived what God has prepared for those who love Him." But I think it's okay to try and imagine what it might be like. After all, God did give us imaginations.

Here's what I picture:

Luke was a superstar here on earth, big, strong, and handsome, and most everywhere he went he was treated pretty special. People looked up to him, and it wasn't hard to notice the looks of respect and admiration he got from those around him.

Just as easily you could see the looks of disrespect, sometimes even disdain, that Johnny would get from strangers who didn't know him. Sometimes he was pretty messy when he ate. Sometimes he talked too loud. Sometimes he hugged people that may not have felt like being hugged.

But often he was with Luke, sometimes holding his hand if there was a crowd and he was feeling nervous. And Luke would give people a look that would put to rest any thought somebody might have of expressing negative thoughts towards Johnny. It was a look that said, "He's with me."

On that awful night in the parking lot when Luke left this life to begin his next one, his eternal one, I like to picture him at the entrance to heaven, surrounded by thousands of people who he doesn't know and don't recognize him. He's wondering how he's ever going to make it through to the gate.

And then he looks up and sees Johnny walking towards him, that big goofy smile on his face. Johnny grabs Luke's hand and looks around at the crowd of faces who stop to watch. "He's with me," Johnny says, and the crowd clears a path as the two brothers walk in together.

A month after Luke's funeral, on a scorching mid-August day, Ellie, Kenny, and I were hanging out in our Oakwood Estates fortress when dad poked his head in.

"Hey guys," he said. "Have any of you heard anything about Bruce Junkers?"

"What do you mean?" I asked.

"Well, he's missing."

"Missing? What do you mean he's missing?"

"They found his car in the Piggly Wiggly parking lot several nights ago, but there's been no sign of him. They think something must have happened to him. They found a bunch of beer bottles in his car, and also some syringes."

"That's weird," Ellie said. "I knew he was a big-time drinker, but I didn't know he was using intravenous drugs."

"I didn't either," dad said. "Anyway, if you hear anything, let me know. The police are looking for him."

As he turned to leave I said, "Dad, I know it's probably not right, but I hope they never find him."

He looked at me with an expression that I couldn't quite read, but then he nodded. "I know."

After he left, Kenny said, "Wow! Syringes. I wonder if somebody drugged him and did something to him."

"It does sound like some foul play was involved," Ellie said.

"Yeah," I added. "I wonder where those syringes could have come from."

And then we sat there quietly for a minute looking at each other, just the three of us: the son of a doctor, the daughter of drug addicts, and an insulin-dependent diabetic.

Finally Ellie asked, "Anybody want to go to Lincoln Lake today?"

"No thanks," I answered. "Maybe not for quite a while."

Sometimes the bad guy loses.

Epilogue

<u>Inauguration Day</u>

"Difficult roads often lead to beautiful destinations." -
Anonymous

I looked in the mirror and combed my hair – wondering again where all the gray had come from – and straightened my tie. Over the years I had gotten used to wearing a tie, but it was still something I would prefer to avoid.

"You look very handsome, Mr. Cateere," she said, walking into the room.

I turned around and looked once again at the most beautiful woman I had ever seen. Her blonde hair was just beginning to show some gray, and her green eyes and smile were still as bright as the day I first saw her at that district track meet almost 35 years earlier.

"Well thank you, Dr. Cateere," I said, "but I think you should be addressing me as Mr. Vice President."

"Oh no, not yet. Not for another hour."

It was Saturday, January 20, 2001, Inauguration Day, and I was about to become the 46th Vice President of the United States. It was eight days before I turned 45, making me the eighth youngest vice president ever. In many ways I still felt like a kid from Bonney Flats, too young for such responsibility, and tried to imagine what John Breckinridge must have been feeling when he became the youngest vice president at the age of 36 in 1857. Wow.

After high school and college I had gone to law school, and then was hired by the King County District Attorney's Office, where eventually I became the lead prosecutor. After 9 years I decided to throw my hat into the political ring and ran for the Washington State Senate, District 31.

I hired Kenny to write all of my commercials, and gave him free reign, except that there could be absolutely no negative attacks. So all of my commercials began like this: "First let me tell you something about my opponent. He is a decent, honest man who loves his family, this state, and our country. Our only differences are political." And then I'd go on to say what I stood for, why I was running, and why people should vote for me.

For some reason, the positive nature of the campaign – which I'll admit wasn't always easy to maintain when I was being attacked – seemed to really resonate with the voters, and in November of 1990, at the age of 34, I was elected to the state senate.

I was re-elected in 1992 and '94, and in 1996 ran for governor in our state. Although I always tried to sound very confident during the campaign, I think I was as surprised as anybody when I won.

In the summer of 2000, as I was entering the final months of my first term as governor, I was chosen at our national convention to be a part of our party's ticket as the vice presidential nomination. And in November we won.

Ellie and I had each spent our whole lives in the state of Washington, and now we were about to move to the other Washington. Northwest to Northeast. Pacific to Atlantic. Seahawks, Sonics, and Mariners to Redskins, Wizards, and Orioles. Trading our four-bedroom, 3,000 square-foot ranch house in Olympia (we chose not to live in the Governor's Mansion while they worked on getting rid of a bat infestation, of all things) for the vice president's residence, a 9,000 square-foot home at Number One Observatory Circle on the grounds of the U.S. Naval Observatory. It was a bit daunting, to say the least.

"So, what are you thinking about on this momentous occasion?" Ellie asked.

"Actually, I was just thinking about Luke," I said. "Tomorrow would be his birthday."

"Yes, I know."

"He should be here. He really should be here."

"Well, if he was here, I know he'd be very proud of you, Mouse," Ellie said. "And he wouldn't be at all surprised."

"But he wouldn't call me Mr. Vice President, would he?"

"No. I think he would call you Mr. Mouse."

We both smiled, thinking about our amazing friend.

"He kind of predicted this, didn't he?" I said.

"Actually, what he said was that you'd be the president someday."

"Well, our new home may not be *the* White House, but it is *a* white house," I countered. "And who knows what the future holds?"

As soon as I said that I had to smile, thinking of something that Mr. Daisy used to always say: "I may not know what the future holds, but I know who holds the future."

We smiled and walked hand-in-hand to the west front of the United States Capitol building where I would recite my oath, which I had pretty well memorized.

"I, Michael Kirk Cateere, do solemnly swear that I will support and defend the constitution of the United States against all enemies, foreign and domestic; that I will bear true faith and allegiance to the same; that I take this obligation freely, without any mental reservation or purpose of evasion; and that I will faithfully discharge the duties of the office on which I am about to enter. So help me God."

It was going to be my great honor to serve under our new president, Art DeKoker. President DeKoker, 15 years my senior, had served honorably during the Vietnam War, been a successful businessman, and then a popular three-term governor of Kansas. He was a man of unquestioned honesty and integrity, and I was very excited about his leadership for this great nation of ours.

After my oath, I looked out over the mall at the inspiring sights of the Washington Monument and, further in the distance, the Lincoln Memorial. And then I turned and looked into the faces of those who were with me, who had shared this incredible journey with me, and who were my true inspirations.

There was Ellie, of course, my dear friend of 34 years and wife for the past 23. She would be continuing her work as a pediatrician in the nearby suburb of Chevy Chase, Maryland.

On each side of her stood our two boys, Lucas, 21, and Jonathan, 19. We were so proud of the fine young men that our sons had become.

To their left was my mom, now 74, still as sharp and active and loving as always. Dad had died of a heart attack in his sleep eight years earlier, just a few months after he had finally sold his medical practice and retired. I miss him every day.

Next to mom was my "second father," Mr. Daisy. Shortly after Mrs. Daisy died, Mr. Daisy had resigned as head pastor of Bonney Flats Baptist Church, turning the leadership over to the youth pastor, Jesse Bradley. Like Mr. Daisy, Jesse was a wonderful man who lived his life according to the verses in Matthew 22: *"Love the Lord your God with all your heart, and with all your soul, and with all your mind. This is the first and greatest commandment. And a second is like it: love your neighbor as yourself."* Bonney Flats Baptist Church was in good hands.

When Mr. Daisy resigned as pastor, he didn't retire, but instead went to the mission field. He said he was inspired by the story of five young missionaries who had been killed in the jungles of Ecuador in 1956, the same year that Luke and Johnny were born. And Luke's death convinced him to make the most of what little time he might have left here. So he went to live and work with the Huanca people group of the Junin Region in central Peru, where he spent the next 20 years of his life.

Since he returned, he and mom had been constant companions. I asked her once if there was anything romantic between the two of them, and she just scoffed. "Michael, he's my brother," she said.

Both Matthew and Mark Daisy were there with their wives, who just happened to be Kenny's oldest sisters. Matthew was married to Alice, and Mark had married Barbara. Kenny said it seemed "very Appalachian" to have his "brothers" marry his sisters, and he insisted that all the Daisy kids (Matthew had 2 and Mark had 3) call him "Uncle Uncle."

Kenny was there in his wheelchair, continuing to defy the doctors' prognosis. He called himself "the world's greatest standup comic who couldn't stand up." His gift of making people laugh was on full display when he co-wrote the screenplay for the 1987 movie *The Princess Bride,* and then as one of the writers for the TV show *Wings.* I had offered him a job as a speechwriter for me, but he said "there's already enough comedy in Washington D.C. politics without my help."

There were others there in my group of supporters – Mr. & Mrs. Carew, former teachers and coaches, friends and teammates from along the way – all people who had made a positive difference in my life. And there were four symbolic empty chairs – one for dad, one for Mrs. Daisy, one for Johnny, and one for the amazing Luke Daisy – without whom none of this would have been possible.

All of the choices we make in life take us down a path that leads to our ultimate destination, which is, of course, the most important thing. And while we are all responsible for those choices we make, they are shaped by the people who God places in our lives. As I looked at those He had placed in mine – including those 4 empty chairs - my heart was overflowing with gratefulness.

All of our paths are marked with laughter and tears, triumph and failure, elation and sorrow. And while we must never lose sight of our final destination, we should always remember to be thankful for our companions along the way, and never forget to find joy - great joy – in the journey that takes us there.

Acknowledgements

Many of the people in this story have the same names as people from the author's life, but all of the characters are fictional and not meant to represent those real people. One of the joys of writing *The Legend of Luke Daisy* was creating the unusual names (Ellie Fent, Ken Carew, Mouse Cateere, Ryan Hosserous, etc.), and assigning side characters the names of people who I have liked and admired.

Likewise, the city of Bonney Flats doesn't exist. Geographically and descriptively it is similar to the city of Federal Way, Washington, where the author grew up, although there was no Paul Revere High School, no Lewis & Clark Junior High, and no Lincoln Lake in the center of town, in which there may or may not be any dead bodies.

The events in the story are also fictional, although folks who grew up with the author will certainly recognize some similarities to actual occurrences. That's called inspiration.

As far as the historical events, every effort was made to be true to the real life happenings of that era. But apologies are due to President George W. Bush and Vice President Dick Cheney, who were the real men inaugurated on January 20, 2001; to William Goldman, the real screenwriter of *The Princess Bride*; to Gary Locke, Washington's real governor in 1996; to Tom Brennan, the real number 4 selection of the Cleveland Indians in the 1974 Major League baseball draft; and to the talented boys from Houston who did, in fact, win the 1966 Little League World Series. They were fortunate to not have to play against Luke.

Many readers, I'm fairly certain, will feel as though they had the best childhood and the greatest group of friends and family growing up. But they are mistaken. Those priceless treasures belong to this author, and are the reason this story was written.

About the Author

Matt McCully is a former sportswriter and a retired air traffic controller. He is a graduate of Thomas Jefferson High School in Federal Way and the University of Puget Sound in Tacoma. He and his wife, Char, live in Enumclaw, Washington, and are members of Grace Community Church in Auburn. They are blessed with two wonderful daughters and son-in-laws, and five terrific grandchildren.

Cover Illustration by Britta Hensley

Made in the USA
San Bernardino, CA
14 May 2019